Internal Quality Auditing

Also Available from ASQ Quality Press

Quality Audits for Improved Performance, Second Edition
Dennis R. Arter

After the Quality Audit: Closing the Loop on the Audit Process,
Second Edition
J.P. Russell and Terry Regel

Fundamentals of Quality Auditing
B. Scott Parsowith

The Quality Audit Handbook, Second Edition
ASQ Quality Audit Division, J.P. Russell, editing director

*Meet the Registrar: Firsthand Accounts of ISO 9000 Success
from the Registration Source*
C. Michael Taylor

The Quality Audit: A Management Evaluation Tool
Charles A. Mills

Quality Management Benchmark Assessment, Second Edition
J.P. Russell

To request a complimentary copy of ASQ Quality Press publications, call 800-246-1946, or visit our online bookstore at http://qualitypress.asq.org.

Internal Quality Auditing

Denis Pronovost

ASQ Quality Press
Milwaukee, Wisconsin

Internal Quality Auditing
Denis Pronovost

Library of Congress Cataloging-in-Publication Data

Pronovost, Denis, 1944–
    Internal quality auditing/Denis Pronovost
        p.   cm.
    Includes bibliographical references and index.
    ISBN 0-87389-476-6 (alk. paper)
        1. Auditing, Internal. I. Title.
HF5668.25.P76 2000   00-022493
657'.458—dc21

10 9 8 7 6 5 4 3 2

ISBN 0-87389-476-6

Acquisitions Editor: Ken Zielske
Project Editor: Annemieke Koudstaal
Production Administrator: Shawn Dohogne
Special Marketing Representative: Matthew Meinholz

ASQ Mission: The American Society for Quality advances individual and organizational performance excellence worldwide by providing opportunities for learning, quality improvement, and knowledge exchange.

Attention: Bookstores, Wholesalers, Schools and Corporations:
ASQ Quality Press books, videotapes, audiotapes, and software are available at quantity discounts with bulk purchases for business, educational, or instructional use. For information, please contact ASQ Quality Press at 800-248-1946, or write to ASQ Quality Press, P.O. Box 3005, Milwaukee, WI 53201-3005.

To place orders or to request a free copy of the ASQ Quality Press Publications Catalog, including ASQ membership information, call 800-248-1946. Visit our web site at www.asq.org.

Printed in the United States of America

 Printed on acid-free paper

American Society for Quality
ASQ®

Quality Press
600 N. Plankinton Avenue
Milwaukee, Wisconsin 53203
Call toll free 800-248-1946
Fax 414-272-1734
www.asq.org
http://qualitypress.asq.org
http://standardsgroup.asq.org
E-mail: authors@asq.org

To Gordon MacKenzie
Who re-kindled the fire, and
To Louise
Who maintained it.

‖ FOREWORD ‖

Hundreds of thousands of organizations worldwide, in all activity sectors, have put into practice the management system approach of international standards such as ISO 9000 and ISO 14000. Beyond the quality and environmental performance objectives of these standards, a growing number of organizations are also applying this approach to other management objectives, such as in the area of occupational health and safety.

Central to any management system, internal auditing serves a number of purposes. It is first and foremost a tool to confirm compliance to the established policies and procedures. It enables the assessment of the effectiveness of the implementation. It may also help significantly in identifying areas for improvement. This later dimension is likely to take a more prominent role as the management system of an organization gains in maturity. In addition, a well-designed and competently implemented audit is a powerful tool to create greater awareness and understanding of the policies, objectives, and procedures of an organization. As a cross-fertilization opportunity, auditing can go beyond the limits of traditional quality assurance and become a catalyst for innovation.

It is rapidly clear as we go from one chapter to the other, that the author is a seasoned auditor able to draw from a wealth of experience. Under his scrutiny, auditing becomes concrete, nononsense, and value-contributing. This book will contribute to a better understanding of what auditing is about. It is easy to consult and rich in practical details. It will be a useful reference for both the experienced and the less experienced auditor.

Pierre F. Caillibot

‖ PREFACE ‖

The auditing function has developed for more than 30 years in a contractual environment, in a framework of supplier audits. This was done on behalf of large organizations, either public or private, that purchased products presenting a high level of risk in their intended use. The armed forces, the aeronautics and aerospace industries, and the electric utilities' building of nuclear power plants come to mind.

From the audited companies' point of view, the audit results often had an impact in terms of workload, on contractually specified penalties, or sometimes on the loss of a bid when the audit was done to grade potential suppliers. The personnel of companies that were often audited developed techniques and tactics that were used to minimize audit findings and their consequences. On the other side, auditors had to develop skills that enabled them to deal with such tactics and reduce their effectiveness. Some of these auditors, because they were wielding real power, became arrogant and smug. As a consequence, the audit atmosphere was often adversarial, and some auditors were saying that the on-site activities were sometimes performed in a *hostile environment*.

The first quality system registrars appeared in the early 1980s, and they naturally employed auditors well versed in customer-supplier audits. Furthermore, the first companies to seek registration were often forced into it by their customers, thus creating the perception that registrars were an arm of the customer and registration audits the same as audits done by customers. Demand for registration grew rapidly in the early 1990s, the number of registrars followed, and the incumbent auditors had to train a large number of new auditors in a short period of time. They passed on their cultural heritage.

Before the ISO 9000 standards were published, only a few large organizations were actually doing internal quality audits, most of them because it was a contractual requirement. In the early 1990s, the ISO 9000 standards were adopted by a growing number of organizations in many countries. As these standards require the implementation of internal quality audits, hundreds of thousands of internal auditors had to be trained, and the sole models were registrar auditors and customer auditors, both having similar methods and techniques. As a result, internal auditors often copied the registration auditors whom they regularly met.

The experience gained in the past 10 years has taught that internal auditing is very different from external auditing. Organizations learned that the duplication of registration or maintenance audits eventually leads to a waste of resources. It was discovered that, once the quality management system has matured, internal audits limited to verifying the compliance of activities to the documentation are a waste of time.

Internal quality audits can be an important part of management. They can provide an unbiased view of the processes that have a direct impact on deliverables, the products and services for which the organization exists. Internal quality audits can deliver very valuable information, which will be fed into management processes that deal with quality orientations, policies, and objectives, as well as quality improvement. For internal quality audits to contribute in such a manner, an effort must be made to redefine the purpose of audits and the methods used.

The purpose of this book is to put forward some ideas and guidelines for more effective internal audits programs, while showing tools often used by internal auditors. It is intended for two different groups of persons: internal audits program managers and persons performing audits in the program. For that reason, it is presented in two sections:

1. Managing the Audit Program

2. Doing an Audit

I hope that this book will help you implement effective internal quality audits.

Denis Pronovost, January 2000

‖ ACKNOWLEDGMENTS ‖

This book is the result of many years of experience and training in internal quality auditing. As much of the experience was by gained by trial and error, my first thanks go to all the companies that allowed me to experiment, especially Hydro-Québec, where I started doing internal audits. I am also much indebted to all the persons who provided valuable comments on a preliminary version. I want to express my deepest gratitude to André Audet and Pierre Lavoie, who spent more hours than I had hoped for, reading and commenting with all the rigor they are capable of.

The standards referenced within the text of this book use the international identification. Below is a list of these standards as well as their US equivalents.

Book Reference	Actual Title (as found in the ASQ Quality Press Bookstore/Catalog)
AS 9000	SAE AS9000-1997
ISO 8402-1994	ANSI/ISO/ASQC A8402-1994
ISO 9001	ANSI/ISO/ASQC Q9001-1994
ISO 9002	ANSI/ISO/ASQC Q9002-1994
ISO 9003	ANSI/ISO/ASQC Q9003-1994
ISO 9004	ANSI/ISO/ASQC Q9004-1-1994, Q9004-2-1991, Q9004-3-1993, Q9004-4-1993
ISO 10011	ANSI/ISO/ASQC Q10011-1994
ISO 14001	ANSI/ISO 14001-1996
ISO 14010	ANS/ISO 14010-1996
ISO 14011	ANSI/ISO 14011-1996
ISO 14012	ANSI/ISO 14012-1996
ISO/DIS 9000:2000	BSR/ISO/DIS 9000:2000

‖ TABLE OF CONTENTS ‖

Section Two: Doing an Audit   63

‖ LIST OF FIGURES ‖

‖ LIST OF TABLES ‖

Section One

Managing the Audit Program

‖ Chapter 1 ‖

Introduction

This first section is intended for persons having responsibility for defining and implementing the internal quality audit program, as well as for persons taking responsibility for managing a pre-established program. The audit program manager has to justify to upper management the use of resources for internal quality audits, as a function of expected results. This internal quality audit program is in itself a system of interrelated processes, producing results at predetermined times. The quantity and quality of these results are in direct relationship to the amount of resources and the implementation methods.

To obtain the most from allocated resources, the program manager must have a good understanding of the forces at play and of the advantages and disadvantages of various alternatives, at the onset of the program and thereafter.

‖ Chapter 2 ‖

Quality Management Systems and Standards

Management System

An internal quality audit program is best initiated when properly positioned in the perspective of the overall organization, thus facilitating the determination of the objectives and scope of the program. The purpose of any organization is to produce desired results, and activities within the organization are structured to achieve these results. The management is the arrangement of resources in order to obtain these results effectively, through a system of interrelated processes, the management system. The organization also *produces* unwanted results, with the objective of keeping these various impacts at a minimum. These objectives and results can be seen as interrelated aspects of a unique system (see Figure 2.1.):

+ Quality, for results demanded by external customers
+ Financial, for results expected by the investors
+ Environment, for environmental impacts caused by the organization's products and activities

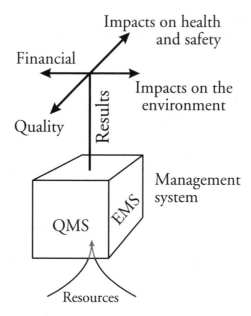

Figure 2.1. Interrelated aspects of an organization.

- ✦ Health and safety, for H&S impacts on workers and others in contact with the organization and its products
- ✦ Others, such as social and political impacts

Any modification in the objectives of one aspect will affect one or more other aspects. Let's look at the example of a dry-cleaning business, which has the following objectives:

- ✦ Cleaning of clothing and other items—quick service (6 hours), normal service (24 hours), or special service
- ✦ Reasonable profits for investors
- ✦ Solid, liquid, and gaseous wastes within applicable regulations
- ✦ Minimal impact on workers' health and safety in using chemicals and equipment

A modification of the process in order to use a cheaper chemical product will have a positive impact on profits. It would also likely have impacts, positive or negative, on the quality of the cleaning, on the workers' health, and on the liquid and gaseous wastes.

It is possible to examine and analyze the management system in the light of each aspect, as if we were looking at a two-dimensional projection of a complex object. Thus, the view of activities and processes from the quality perspective—that is, results expected by customers—will show the quality management system (QMS). Similarly, the view from the environmental impacts perspective shows the environmental management system (EMS).

Standards

Hundreds of documents are available, in many languages, for use by managers to guide their efforts. Some of these documents deal with management tools and techniques in general; others are aimed at one aspect of the management system. The best known are, for the environmental management aspect:

+ Responsible Care
+ ISO 14001
+ EMAR (Eco-Management Audit Regulation)

and for the quality management aspect:

+ MIL-Q-9858, CAN-Z-299 Series, AQAP Series, much used in previous decades
+ ISO 9001:1994[1] and derived standards, such as QS-9000, ISO 13485:1996 ISO/IEC 17025:2000, and SAE AS 9000
+ HACCP (Hazard Analysis Critical Control Point)
+ ISO 9004:1994
+ Malcolm Baldrige National Quality Award
+ Criteria for the Canada Awards for Excellence

In the quality aspect, the MIL-Q-9858, CAN-Z-299 Series, AQAP Series, ISO 9001 and derived standards, including HACCP, can be prescribed by a customer or by a competent jurisdiction to obtain an adequate level of confidence in the products. Other standards are not meant to be used in such a way. ISO 9004 contains guidelines for a quality management system, whereas the Malcolm Baldrige and other similar national criteria are designed as a tools to measure and improve an organization's overall performance. These criteria are often referred to as total quality management models.

Typically, larger organizations use two types of quality management standards:

+ ISO 9001 and/or derived standards, including HACCP, in order to improve their relationship with their customers and with the market, as well as to satisfy regulatory requirements
+ ISO 9004, or a national or regional total quality model, in order to continuously improve results, processes, and management systems

Smaller organizations often focus on ISO 9001 and derived standards, driven by their markets. Very small organizations do not generally use quality management standards, except when forced to do so by one or more customers.

ISO 9001 is therefore the best known and most used standard, but one must realize that other standards are available that are compatible with ISO 9001. And, whenever one sees ISO 9001 or the name of a derived standard, one automatically thinks registration or certification by an independent body. Therefore, internal quality auditing is often perceived as an activity limited to registered organizations; however, internal management auditing has been around for decades in all large public organizations.

Audit Standards

The audit of a quality management system consists of a set of complex activities, and standards can help in managing and performing these activities. The ISO 10011 standard proposes guidelines for performing audits, for managing the program and for qualifying auditors, related to QMS audits. The ISO 14010,

ISO 14011, and ISO 14012 standards propose similar guidelines for EMS audits. All the above audit guidelines are in the process of being merged into a single standard, ISO 19011. At the time of writing this book, it had reached the status of first committee draft (CD1). Before reaching the status of international standard, ISO/CD1 19011 still has to go through many phases of commenting and voting. In its present form, it is a notable improvement from ISO 10011.

In addition to these international standards, other international, national, and private standards are available for further guidance. Furthermore, National Auditor Certification schemes and some auditor associations provide guidelines and criteria that can be used as input into the process of qualifying internal auditors.

Note

1. The expression ISO 9001 includes ISO 9002.

‖ Chapter 3 ‖

Terminology

Introduction

Before going further, let's clarify some terms, acronyms, and expressions that will be used frequently in this book. Many documents deal with the terminology in the quality field. The best known are:

- ✦ ISO/IEC Guide 2:1996 from the International Organization for Standardization (ISO)
- ✦ ISO 8402:1994 and ISO/DIS 9000:2000
- ✦ ISO 9001:1994 and ISO/DIS 9001:2000
- ✦ ISO 10011-1:1990 and ISO/CD1 19011:2001

The quality-related terminology is rapidly evolving with the revision of the ISO 9000 family and of the audit standards. As much as possible, I have used here the terms as defined in the latest edition of the standards, with the exception of a few terms related to the audit process, explained in the following paragraphs.

Acronyms and Expressions

In order to keep the text simple, the acronym QMS is used to mean quality management system, as are the following short expressions:

✦ Program or audit program = internal quality audits program

✦ Audit or internal audit = internal quality audit

Furthermore, the terms *organization* and *company* are interchangeable. *Organization* is defined as any "group of people and facilities with an orderly arrangement of responsibilities, authorities and relationships."[1] Examples are a corporation, a plant, a group, an institution, a sector, and a department.

Audit Terminology

Some of the terms in the standards are confusing, especially *audit* and *lead auditor*. For the audit process, we will use the terms shown in Figure 3.1, which clearly separates the activities and responsibilities of the program manager from those of the team for each audit. As a consequence, Figure 3.1 also refers to the two sections of this book.

The term *audit* is frequently misused to describe one phase of the audit, in which information is gathered and conclusions are drawn. Some books and standards use *on-site auditing activities* or *on-site activities,* a practice that creates confusion. In order to avoid confusion while keeping things simple, this book will use the term *inquiry* for that phase of the audit. *The American Heritage Dictionary* defines *inquiry* as:

1. The act of inquiring

2. A question; a query

3. A close examination of a matter in a search for information or truth[2]

The third definition applies well to the function of an auditor.

All the terms related to the various phases of the audit are presented schematically in Figure 3.1. The term *follow-up audit* is used to describe the verification of a corrective action raised at a previous audit. ISO/CD1 19011 has a clause (6.6) on "audit follow-up," which includes the auditee's determination and initi-

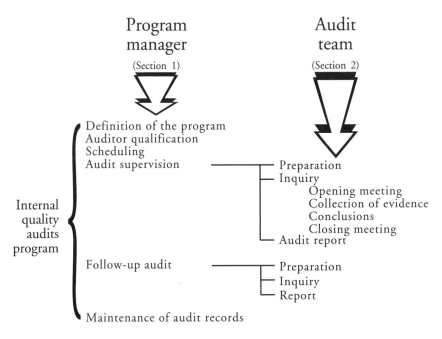

Figure 3.1. Hierarchy of audit-related terms.

ation of any corrective action, as well as the verification of the corrective action. This clause opens the door to a less rigorous verification of audit corrective actions, in that:

1. This verification does not need to be done under the audit program authority.

2. This verification need not be an audit, although it may lead to additional audits.

I strongly believe that the verification of any corrective action done as a result of an audit should be done under the authority of the audit program and that it should be systematic in:

1. Preparation: understanding the nature and extent of the audit nonconformity and the implemented corrective action

Auditor qualifications*	Functions in audit team
Supervisor	
Senior (lead) auditor	Team leader
Auditor	Auditor
Provisional auditor	Observer
	Technical expert

*As adopted by the International Auditor and Training Certification Association (IATCA).

Table 3.1.   Auditor qualifications and functions.

2. Inquiry: obtaining objective evidence about the implementation of the corrective action and coming to conclusions about its compliance and effectiveness

3. Reporting: describing the conclusions

Since these three phases are essentially those of an audit, I use the expression *follow-up audit* to describe this process.

There is another area in which the same term is used with two meanings in ISO 10011. The term *lead auditor* is often used both for a level of auditor qualification and for the function of leading an audit team. In agreement with ISO/CD1 19011, this book will use the term *team leader* for the function of leading a team, keeping lead auditor/senior auditor for a qualification level. ISO 10011:1990 also uses the term *auditor* both for a level of qualification and for a function in the team. This does not, however, create much confusion. This book will use the terms listed in Table 3.1. The functions in an audit team are certainly related to the qualifications but should not be confused with them.

Notes

1. From ISO/DIS 9000:2000

2. Excerpted from *The American Heritage Dictionary of the English Language, Third Edition* Copyright © 1992 by Houghton Mifflin Company. Electronic version licensed from Lernout & Hauspie Speech Products N.V., further reproduction and distribution restricted in accordance with the Copyright Law of the United States. All rights reserved.

‖ Chapter 4 ‖

Objectives and Scope of the Audit Program

External Audit vs. Internal Audit

Quality auditing is essentially a verification activity. What is verified, and in reference to what? Many subjects are inter-related: the quality management external standard, the organization's objectives and expected results, the system and process documentation, and the actual activities and results. Figure 4.1 shows the six possible verification activities around four subjects.

When the external reference is ISO 9001, or one of its derived standards, most organizations use the services of an external verification firm, a registrar. This registrar limits its verification to the activities of the QMS that have a direct impact on the organization's quality objectives. The registrar verification questions:

+ Have clear objectives been defined, and are they under-stood and maintained (in Figure 4.1) [1]?

+ Does the process documentation cover all the clauses of the standard [2]?

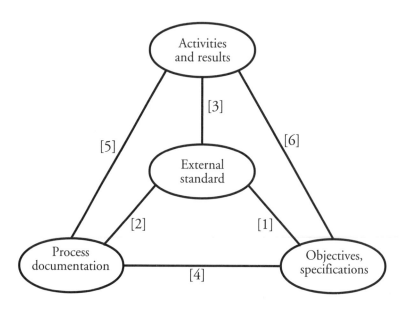

Figure 4.1. Multiple verification activities around a quality management system.

+ Are activities
    + Capable of meeting the requirements of the standard [3]?
    + In compliance with the documentation [5]?
+ Are results measured and related to the objectives [6]?

Relation [4] questions if methods are able to achieve the objectives efficiently, and this verification is not covered by a registrar[1].

Over and above external audits done by a registrar, some organizations see their QMS audited by one or more customers, which is another type of external audit. The purpose, the scope, and the resources allocated for that type of audit may be very different from those of a registrar.

Does that mean that internal auditing should be limited to the verification of the capability of the methods and processes [4]? Of course not, for many reasons:

1. The registrar verification is limited to the activities that have a direct impact on the products, as well as on customer confidence in those products.

2. The registrar spends only a few persons × days on an annual or biannual audit, and the sampling provides only a general view of the QMS.

For these reasons, it is imperative that the organization implement and use a tool for a more comprehensive verification of the QMS, the internal quality audits. This internal tool must take into account all external audits in order to maximize the efficiency of allocated resources.

Objectives for the Internal Audit Program

When external traditional registration audits are performed on the organization, the internal audits program should consider only the following:[2]

+ The compliance of activities to predefined methods and procedures [5]
+ The effectiveness of activities in achieving expected results [6]
+ The efficiency of the processes in achieving the results in the most economical manner [4]

However, the adequacy of the QMS to the external standard [1], [2], and [3] should be assessed under the authority of the internal audits program if one of the following conditions exists:

1. The organization is not audited by a registrar and wishes to self-declare that its QMS conforms to the requirements of the external standard.

2. The organization is registered under a yet-to-be-defined lighter registration scheme, where the scope of surveillance audits would be limited to the same key elements of the QMS and where the registrar would rely on the internal audits program to obtain confidence that the QMS meets all the requirements of the external standard.

The ISO 9001:1994 and derived standards explicitly require that, at a minimum, compliance [5] and effectiveness [6] be audited. The verification of efficiency can also be performed through the audit program, but organizations generally mandate this to other groups, using techniques such as value analysis, process mapping, benchmarking, and re-engineering.

Judging from clause 8.2.2 of the DIS, the next edition of ISO 9001 will probably require that internal audits verify the effective implementation and maintenance of the QMS, which may be interpreted as being different from verifying the effectiveness of the QMS. With such a slanted phrasing and ensuing interpretation, the assessment of effectiveness would be left to top management in its management review process, called for in clause 5.6. Although the new wording adds flexibility and compatibility to an organization's management system, it does not prevent top management from discharging part or all of this responsibility to internal auditors. A balanced approach here could be ideal: asking internal auditors to assess the effectiveness of individual business processes while having the management review look at the effectiveness of the entire system.[3]

Although smaller organizations with a mature QMS mandate internal auditors to assess the compliance and effectiveness of the processes, it is possible to separate these two types of assessment:

1. Internal auditors verify compliance [5].

2. Another person or an internal committee verifies effectiveness [6].

The latter approach is most appropriate for larger organizations, especially those that already perform process and/or product audits at the time they implement QMS internal audits. Through the analysis of information from multiple sources (Figure 4.2), including external audits, a committee can identify the most profitable improvement efforts. The output of this analysis would be a valuable input to the continual improvement process referred to in clause 8.5.1 of ISO/DIS 9001:2000.

To summarize, three approaches are most used in assessing compliance, effectiveness, and efficiency. The choice of approach to be used depends on the size of the organization and on management style.

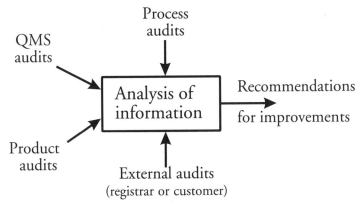

Figure 4.2. Improvements from multiple sources.

Scope of the Internal Audit Program

An organization also has to decide on the scope of the program—
that is, which activities and processes will eventually be subjected to audits. It is the responsibility of upper management to
decide on the size of the program, taking into account the overall quality objectives and relative importance of each process as
it relates to quality objectives.

For an organization whose QMS is registered to ISO 9001,
the internal audit program must include at least all activities
and processes covered by the reference standard. Over and
above this minimum requirement, upper management may
want to extend the scope to all activities and processes in the
QMS perspective. A common practice is to initiate the internal
audit program with a scope limited to the minimum required by
the standard, extending the scope to the overall QMS once the
audit program has reached a level of maturity.

Figure 4.3 shows how system, process, and product audits can
be structured in organizations of various sizes. Typically, smaller
organizations limit themselves to QMS audits, which verify both
the compliance and effectiveness of internal processes.

Larger organizations are likely to perform compliance quality audits, as well as process and/or product audits. The audit

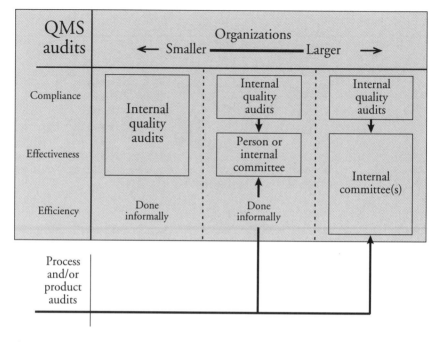

Figure 4.3. Types of audits vs. size of an organization.

results are fed to one or more committees, which draw conclusions on the effectiveness and efficiency of the QMS.

It is important to realize that all decisions on the objectives and on the scope of the internal quality audit program have a direct impact on the resources required to carry out the audits, especially on the quantity and competence of human resources (covered in chapter 5).

Relationships with the Organization

The internal quality audit program is influenced by many groups that are external to the program, and it produces results that are used by many groups. Figure 4.4 shows some of the groups that are closely connected to the internal audits.

The scheduling process, the beginning of the cycle, has the most important inputs, and this process is under the responsibility of the program manager. The important outputs—that is,

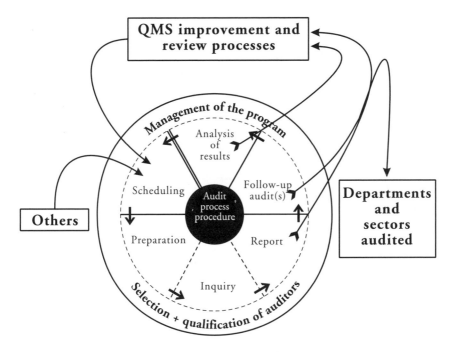

Figure 4.4. Internal audits in relationships with the organization.

audit conclusions presented in the audit report and the results of any follow-up audits—are naturally at the end of the cycle. These outputs, along with the analysis of audit results, are critical inputs into the QMS improvement and review process. (The scheduling of audits and the analysis of results are covered in chapters 8 and 9, and audit results are discussed in chapters 15 and 16.)

Joint Audits

Quality management system internal auditing has been around for more than a decade. The practice of internally auditing an environmental management system has gained momentum in the past decade, and it is likely that internal auditing will also be used eventually in other aspects of a management system. The next wave of management standards could very well be on occupational health and safety.

As each new family of standards is published, it is implemented by specialists in a more or less harmonized way with the previous wave. The inevitable consequence is that internal audit programs for quality, environment, and O.H.&S. will remain separated for many years. But this does not preclude the realization of joint audits. On the contrary, doing joint audits internally will promote the harmonization of these various management systems for increased effectiveness.

If joint internal audits are planned, the organization should carefully define the objectives and scopes of each audit program, so that they are compatible. Special consideration should be given to the specific responsibilities of each organization and to the audit methods and interfaces. Also, the leading of a joint audit implies additional responsibilities for the audit team leader, which should be reflected in the qualification requirements.

Notes

1. In some accreditation schemes, this aspect is also covered.

2. Although ISO/DIS 9001:2000 requires the internal audits to verify the conformance of the QMS to the standard, I believe it need not be done again if done by a registrar.

3. For more information on processes and systems, see the quality management principles in clause 0.2 of ISO/DIS 9000:2000 or in clause 4.3 of ISO/DIS 9004:2000.

| Chapter 5 |

Human Resources

Amount of Resources

The amount of resources that should be allocated to internal quality auditing depends mainly on the size of the organization, on the objectives of the internal audits, on the scope of the program, and on the depth of the verification. A survey of a few industrial and commercial companies, in both goods and services sectors, reveals a weak correlation (see Figure 5.1) between the number of employees and the number of persons × days taken to perform internal quality audits.[1,2]

Resource Use

Managing the Audit Program

The responsibility for managing the internal quality audit program is most often assigned to the person in charge of supervising the entire QMS—the management representative, in ISO 9000 terminology. In other cases, this responsibility is discharged to a person reporting directly to the management representative.

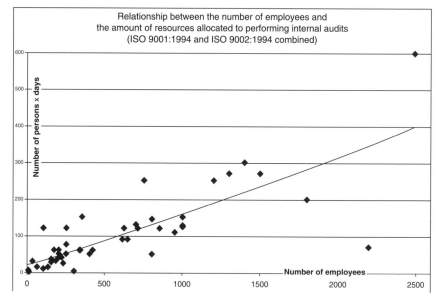

Figure 5.1. Audit resources vs. number of employees.

Doing the Audits

Small Organizations

The number of persons × days being minimal, usually less than 10, internal quality audits are generally performed by the program manager, who is also the management representative.

Medium-Size Organizations

In the range of 10 to 100 persons × days, the workload can be important for a single auditor, being close to a full-time assignment in larger organizations. There is also the risk that this single auditor may become unavailable for a long period of time—a departure or long illness, for example. This would force the organization to train a replacement from scratch, while having to cancel or postpone planned audits. This situation could jeopardize an ISO 9000 registration if the organization does not have an operating internal audits program for many months.

In order to reduce or eliminate this risk, medium-size organizations usually develop a small team of two to five auditors. These supplementary auditors are trained to prepare, do, and report audits, within the framework of the program, supported by the manager. They are then used for one or two days a couple of times a year.

Large Organizations

The number of persons × days being often above 100, it becomes impractical, and very risky, to have only one internal auditor. A large organization should train at least a few auditors besides the program manager. However, many large organizations decide to train a large number of internal auditors. For example, a site of 1000 employees could create a group of 20 internal auditors, each removed from their regular jobs 5 to 10 days per year to perform internal audits.

But one must be careful not to go overboard with the number of internal auditors. A greater number of auditors implies that each one contributes fewer audit-days per year. Pushing this to the limit, an auditor spending only one day per year could not maintain auditing skills at an acceptable level. Should that happen, the program manager would have to compensate for this weakness with other mechanisms, such as closer supervision or pre-audit training.

Internal Auditors: A Few or Many?

Medium-size and large organizations have to decide how many internal auditors to train initially. It is not a binary decision between too few and too many but, rather, a position on a continuum. Let's look in Table 5.1 at the advantages and drawbacks of the extremes.

Many organizations initiate their internal audits with only a few auditors, in order to develop the group's knowledge and skills, and then gradually increase the number of auditors through internal or external training.

Unique auditor ←	→ Large number of auditors
Cost of initial training and of an eventual replacement is low	Cost for initial training, for maintenance, and for replacement of auditors is substantially higher
Auditor becomes very efficient	Audit experience being limited, each auditor maintains a minimal ability
Auditor requires no support, and only negligible supervision	Better support and supervision is required, as well as more detailed audit methods
Audit scheduling is very simple	The scheduling of audits and of auditors is much more complex
Loss of auditor has a high negative impact	Loss of one of the auditors has negligible impact; loss of program manager will not disrupt audit schedule
Auditor may be perceived as the QMS "police"	This is a negligible risk since auditors come from many departments
	This is an excellent way to promote the quality concepts and the QMS; auditors gain knowledge of other functions of the organization
	Auditors are more likely to perceive the organization as a system of interrelated processes
	It promotes cross-pollination of good practices within the organization

Table 5.1. Advantages and drawbacks vs. number of auditors.

Notes

1. In all cases, claimed objectives include compliance and effectiveness; the depth of verification cannot be quantified or assigned attributes.

2. There seems to be little difference between organizations registered to ISO 9001:1994 and those registered to ISO 9002:1994; the survey did not include ISO 9003 registered organizations.

‖ Chapter 6 ‖

Auditor Qualification and Competence

Purpose

The processes for the selection and training of auditors have as their objective that the audit program can rely on persons having the required competence. It is generally believed that the qualification requirements for internal auditors are lower than those for external auditors, possibly resulting in internal auditors being less competent than external auditors. I strongly disagree with this view. Each type of auditor needs a different set of skills and knowledge. For example, an internal auditor needs better interpersonal skills than an external auditor, because an internal auditor has to maintain a good working relationship with other employees after the audit.

The common meaning of the terms *qualification* and *competence* are used in this book—qualification is used for both the process of qualifying and the minimal result, whereas competence is the possession of attributes, skills, and knowledge to a variable degree. Qualification is different from competence, although they usually go hand-in-hand. But it is possible that a competent person would not have a required qualification, and also that a qualified person could be incompetent. *The American Heritage Dictionary of the English Language* defines these terms as follows:[1]

Qualification

1. The act of qualifying or the condition of being qualified
2. A quality, an ability, or an accomplishment that makes a person suitable for a particular position or task

Competence

1. The state or quality of being adequately or well qualified; ability
2. A specific range of skill, knowledge, or ability

Competence

Competence can be expressed along three interrelated axes: personal attributes and attitudes, skills, and knowledge. For each axis, the requirements depend on (see chapter 4):

1. The scope of the internal audits program
2. The objectives set for internal auditing
3. The role of the person on the audit team

The following are some requirements for each axis.[2]

Personal Attributes and Attitudes

Desirable attributes, which are the source of attitudes and behaviors, are independent of the internal audit's scope and objectives. Anyone wishing to be an auditor should possess:

1. A high level of personal integrity or honesty, which will help in:
    + Making adequate judgments in various situations
    + Being sincere and honest in professional relations
    + Fully committing oneself to the purpose of the audit
2. A sense of self-security that is independent of external factors; this self-esteem enables the auditor to:
    + Be able to really listen to others and to be open-minded about other ways of doing things

+ Show an adequate combination of flexibility and tenacity according to circumstances
+ Stay calm and be objective
+ Make decisions when required, even on partial information

3. Self-control of one's behaviors in order to help the audit process and to be tactful.

All persons involved in the internal audits program should show these attributes and qualities, but they should be more visible on persons having to lead an audit team.

Skills and Abilities

Basic Skills

Some skills are independent of the objectives and scope of audits and of the role of the auditor on the team. The most obvious are related to the capacity to:

+ Read and understand documentation, on paper or in an electronic medium
+ Plan and organize one's own work
+ Understand and adapt to various environments
+ Communicate verbally in an effective way at all levels of the organization
+ Phrase simple and clear questions that are focused on the desired information
+ Listen attentively and understand verbal information
+ Synthesize ideas and manipulate data
+ Operate effectively under moderate stress

Specific Skills

Supplementary skills are required to take the role of team leader and/or if the audit objectives include the verification of process effectiveness. These skills overlap, as shown in Figure 6.1. These supplementary skills are:

Objectives / Role	Compliance	Effectiveness
Auditor	Basic skills	Basic + ❶
Team leader	Basic + ❶ + ❷	

Figure 6.1. Skills vs. audit objectives and role of person.

❶

+ To understand quality objectives related to the processes and to the system
+ To analyze facts and data and to come to adequate conclusions

❷

+ To communicate in writing concisely and clearly
+ To plan, organize, and lead a small team
+ To chair meetings with tact and determination
+ To propose adequate solutions in situations of conflict or important stress

Knowledge

The knowledge required by organizations for their internal auditors is often insufficient, resulting in incomplete or unreliable audit conclusions. An internal auditor has to analyze complex, interrelated processes and to deal with management issues, even more so with the ISO/DIS 9000:2000 family of standards, with its emphasis on management and interrelated processes.

Basic Knowledge

An internal auditor must have completed at least a secondary education and must have some years of experience in positions involving judgment, problem solving, and communication. This minimum should be increased if the audit objectives include the assessment of effectiveness and/or if the internal auditor acts as team leader.

Specific Knowledge

As with skills, some specific knowledge is required to contribute to even a simple audit. An auditor must know:

+ The quality principles that form the basis of any QMS
+ The general audit concepts and techniques, including the type of audits, the approaches and processes, and the subsequent activities, as they relate to internal quality audits
+ The audit process actually implemented in the organization, including forms to be used
+ The processes under audit—that is, the required activities, equipment, personnel qualifications, monitoring, inputs, and so on

Further, an auditor must have minimal knowledge of the industrial sector in which the organization is operating.

Advanced Knowledge

If an auditor has a mandate to assess the effectiveness of the processes, he or she must have a good knowledge of the purpose of each audited process and of how each process relates to other surrounding processes. Furthermore, in order to act as team leader, an auditor must possess a good understanding of the overall QMS, as well as of the organization's quality objectives.

Most of the required knowledge, basic to advanced, is acquired through experience and formal training. However, some knowledge is acquired as part of the preparation of each audit.

Criteria for the Selection of Auditors

An organization obtains potentially competent auditors through applying adequate criteria when initially selecting auditors, followed with appropriate training. As some personal attributes and skills are more difficult to acquire through training, the criteria should be carefully crafted and applied in order to obtain personnel with proper attitudes and skills. It is also possible to raise the selection bar higher than the minimal requirements in order to reduce the subsequent training effort.

In practice, a large number of organizations screen from their personnel individuals who satisfy the following criteria:

+ Have all desired personal attributes and attitudes
+ Have skills related to the capacity to listen carefully to others, to understand complex systems, and to synthesize ideas
+ Have knowledge of the industrial or service sector

Other skills and knowledge are then acquired through formal training.

Training of Auditors

What is the best way to train internal auditors—classroom or on-the-job training? Using external specialized resources or doing it internally? The best solution for any organization depends on many variables:

1. Knowledge and skills to be acquired
2. Initial training effort or training of replacement auditors
3. Number of persons to be trained
4. Human and financial resources available

Initial Training

When initiating the internal audits program, an organization usually does not have access to appropriate expertise internally. External resources must be called upon.

At a minimum, the audit program manager should attend intensive auditor training, a five-day course or equivalent, available through commercial or public schools. If the organization can afford it, a second person should attend similar training: in addition to having a back-up, the interaction between the two persons will reinforce the audit program.

For an organization that needs only two internal auditors, the initial training is now complete. For the training of more internal auditors, the organization has to decide whether to use external specialists or to ask the previously trained auditors to provide internal training (see the decision diagram in Figure 6.2.). The decision to go external or internal will take into account:

+ The geographical distance from available qualified audit specialists
+ The number of auditors to be trained; a large number may justify the cost of an internal auditor training program
+ The availability of an internal auditor training course in another unit of the organization
+ The possibility of purchasing a commercial course to be presented internally

Each approach has its own merits, as summarized in Table 6.1.

Creating a new course internally requires resources, the amount of which is often underestimated. For only a few trainees, most of the learning can be achieved through on-the-job training—that is, going along with an experienced auditor. For a large number of trainees, a classroom approach with practical test cases is preferable. The purchase of an external training package should also be considered. Proper modifications would be required in such a case, and the amount of modification work could be important.

Most organizations use external resources for the initial training effort, to ensure that internal auditing starts on the right track. For a few candidates, sending them to one or more public courses is usually the least expensive solution. For more than 10 candidates, it is generally more practical and less costly to contract the training to a specialized firm that will adapt its

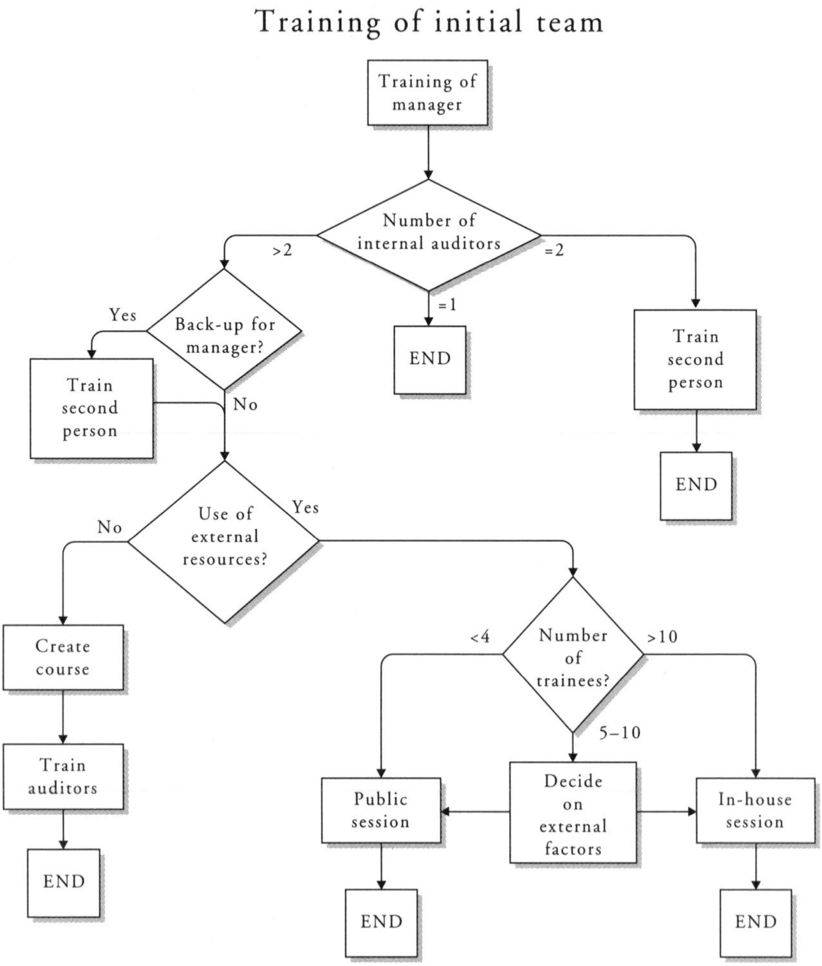

Training of initial team

Figure 6.2. Decision diagram for initial training effort.

standard material to suit the organization. Between 5 and 10 candidates, the costs associated with both public and in-house courses should be assessed, also taking into consideration other factors such as the required simultaneous availability of all trainees for an in-house course, as well as the distance and travel costs to locations where public sessions are held.

Internal resources	External resources
Training well matched to needs— appropriate training methods	No development costs— limited adaptation costs
Reduced costs for delivery of training	Connected to international best practices
Flexibility in scheduling of training sessions	More experienced instructors

Table 6.1. Benefits comparison between internal and external resources for training.

Training of Replacement Auditors

Natural attrition, rotation of personnel, and evolution of each auditor's personal interests require the training of new auditors, on a more or less planned fashion. The methods used in the initial training effort greatly influence how replacement auditors receive proper training.

Organizations that maintain one or two auditors normally send every new auditor to the same or a similar external course. Organizations that have created their own course, or those that have purchased and modified an external course, train their new auditors with the same material as the need arises. These organizations that use external resources for their initial training effort can either use the same external resources or internally train new auditors, a decision based on:

+ The number of persons to be trained each year or each semester
+ The geographical distance from locations where public training is available, as well as related travel costs
+ The flexibility in scheduling the training
+ The availability of competent trainers internally

Assesment of Competence

Once the organization has defined the criteria for initial auditor selection, as well as the skills and knowledge to be acquired through training, it is useful and necessary to specify the methods to be used for the evaluation of each candidate against the selection criteria, and for the acquisition of skills and knowledge.[3]

Candidate Selection

Evaluating personnel is a complex activity, and very often specialists from the human resources or the training department will be able to help. Even when that is the case, auditors are frequently selected on personal impressions or with vague criteria related to attitudes or behaviors. For very small organizations, this may be the only practical method. In such cases, however, all employees know each other rather well, which facilitates the selection process.

The difficulty of the internal auditors' selection process depends largely on the number of new auditors needed annually and on the availability of specialized HR personnel. Personnel evaluation can use fairly complex techniques. The following pages discuss two methods of defining and documenting auditor selection, with various levels of complexity.

Basic Mechanism
The selection criteria should be listed with a sufficient level of detail (usually in the internal audit procedure) and used to select the candidates:

> Candidates who volunteer as internal auditors will be selected on the basis of their personality (attitudes and behaviors), their experience (minimum of five years in the field), their effectiveness in verbal communication, their ability to communicate in writing and to understand written and software documentation.

If a qualification record is needed, it can be as simple as that shown in Figure 6.3. The same record can be used to keep track of training and progression toward team leader status.

Elaborate Mechanism
With the help of human resources specialists, the personal attributes of candidates could undergo formal evaluation, using role-playing, structured tests, interviews with the candidates, and feedback from colleagues. This evaluation could contain some "elimination" criteria as well as measurable personal char-

	Verbal communication	Attitudes and behaviors	Written communication	Experience, five years min.	Observer on one audit	Internal/external training	Etc. . . .	Leading capabilities	Done X audits	Etc. . . .
			Initial selection			Training		Team leader		
Candidate #1										
Candidate #2										
Candidate #3										
Etc. . . .										

Figure 6.3. Simple auditor qualification record.

acteristics. For this latter case, a more complex form can be used for grading the potential of each candidate. An example is shown in Figure 6.4.

Training

Evaluating the training is easier than evaluating a candidate's personal attributes. If training requirements consist of *participating* in one or more courses, an attendance sheet and/or a certificate of attendance constitutes a sufficient record. If each candidate must acquire knowledge or skills, then that requirement should be measured as objectively as possible.

Acquiring Knowledge

The classical method is to use a written exam, and most training organizations have such exams. Knowledge acquisition can also be measured through an interview, which is a more practical method for organizations that do not use external resources to train internal auditors. The interview method, however, will lack the necessary objectivity if not supported by a checklist and marking grid.

Acquiring Skills

The two usual methods are role-playing and observing a candidate while performing the activity. Role-playing is used mostly

Name: _____ Employee #: _____

Department: _____ Tel.: _____

	Characteristic	Grade	Remarks	By / date
Elimination criteria	Education Experience Pass/fail			
	Integrity Honesty Pass/fail			
	Self-control Pass/fail			
	Communication Reading/writing Pass/fail			
Evaluation	Verbal communication 1 to 3, 3 = very clear			
	Stability Objectivity 1 to 3			
	Curiosity Tenacity/flexibility 1 to 3			
	Experience in the industrial sector 1 = 3 to 5 yrs 2 = 5 to 10 yrs 3 = >10 yrs			
	Knowledge QMS + ISO 9000 1 to 3			
	Knowledge of audit techniques 1 to 3			
	Experience as auditor/auditee 1 = auditee 2 = observer 3 = auditor			
	Total			

Figure 6.4. Complete auditor qualification record.

in structured training; observing a candidate is also used in structured training that includes a real audit, as well as in on-the-job training. It is worth noting that the role-playing in structured training can also be used to assess some personal attributes, such as emotional stability, capacity to work under stress, and verbal communication skills.

Auditor Certification Programs

Many programs are available for the certification of registrar auditors, from associations, governmental agencies, and other not-for-profit organizations. Although organizations can use these programs to confirm internal auditor competence, the requirements for obtaining and maintaining such certification are very stringent and usually are not within reach of the average internal auditor.

Some organizations are offering auditor certification adapted to internal auditors. The American Society for Quality (ASQ) has been running the Certified Quality Auditor (CQA) scheme for more than 10 years. More recently, many organizations providing registrar auditor certification have added a different scheme for the certification of internal auditors. These simplified programs can be used to confirm the qualification of internal auditors.

Notes

1. Excerpted from *The American Heritage Dictionary of the English Language, Third Edition.* Copyright © 1992 by Houghton Mifflin Company. Electronic version licensed from Lernout & Hauspie Speech Products N.V., further reproduction and distribution restricted in accordance with the Copyright Law of the United States. All rights reserved.

2. ISO/CD1 19011 proposes minimum requirements for auditors.

3. ISO/CD1 19011 proposes methods for assessing competence.

‖ Chapter 7 ‖

Maintaining Auditor Competence

Objective

An acceptable level of competence and performance must be maintained by internal auditors, through various methods.

Axes of Competence

Of the three axes identified in chapter 6—personal attributes, skills, and knowledge—only the last two are of concern. Skills wear off, and knowledge needs to be updated on a regular basis. Also, auditor certification programs require for maintenance of certification that auditors engage in professional development activities each year, over and above performing audits. The maintenance of individual auditor competence must be coordinated with the maintenance of homogeneity/consistency between auditors.

Audit Skills

The most effective method of maintaining audit skills is to perform audits on a regular basis. Three evenly spaced one-day audits per year is a bare minimum to maintain skills at a minimal level. It is preferable to do twice as much—that is, more than six audit-days per year.

Some organizations use their internal auditors once per year, for a one-day or two-day audit. Audit results are not reliable without complementary activities. In the absence of frequent audits, other activities, such as the following, must be carried out to maintain competence:

+ A one-day annual training session, using practical test cases or role-playing
+ When preparing for each audit, a meeting of the audit team with a qualified resource
+ Participation in audit-related external events, such as conferences and congresses, and associations

Knowledge

The previous discussion on audit skills—that doing audits on a regular basis is the best way to maintain the knowledge related to the quality management system—also applies to the audit methods and to the organization's audit procedure. On the other hand, there is one area of knowledge that has to be updated regularly, no matter how many audits are performed.

The QMS evolves with time, and all auditors and/or team leaders need to be fed with the resulting information. Typical changes in the QMS are:

+ New or modified quality-related policies
+ New quality-related objectives
+ Modified responsibilities and authorities
+ Changes to the audit process itself

These subjects can be added to the agenda of the annual auditor training session, covered individually with each auditor or group of auditors, or can be presented at the audit team meeting before each audit.

Homogeneity

For a given audit, an auditor is asked to make a judgment on the compliance and effectiveness of one or more processes. In identical circumstances, would another auditor reach the same conclusions? Would the same auditor reach the same conclusions at another time, given no variation in the process? These are the two axes of homogeneity of auditors' conclusions. And this concern is twofold for each axis. The inquiry into a business process can be viewed as two successive mental activities, as shown in Figure 7.1:

1. Obtaining a reasonable quantity of factual evidence and findings about a real process

2. Coming to conclusions on compliance and effectiveness from those findings

For a given process, with identical circumstances, there is *homogeneity between auditors* if they come to identical conclusions, despite different sampling and different findings. There is *homogeneity in time* if the same auditor comes to identical conclusions at different times.

It is possible to evaluate the homogeneity of a group of auditors by comparing the audit results of the auditors individually auditing the same process at the same time. But such a procedure

Figure 7.1. Two steps in an inquiry.

would be very time-consuming, both for the auditors and auditee, and hardly feasible. And it is impossible to evaluate homogeneity in time because process conditions normally change with time, and there is no way to tell if different audit results are due to the audited process or to the auditor. Since homogeneity cannot be readily measured, it is necessary to implement methods that will assure a certain level of confidence.

For registrars, homogeneity is a major concern because auditors deal with a large number of organizations. Within a given organization, a manager of internal audits may be tempted to overlook this issue, and doing so can result in the internal audits program slowly becoming ineffective.

Homogeneity Between Auditors

One or more of the following techniques can be used to maintain or improve the homogeneity between auditors:

+ Having detailed audit procedures and methods, which will ensure that auditors collect a sufficient amount of factual data and information

+ Adequately supervising how audits are performed, as well as reviewing audit results

+ In a workshop, asking each auditor to come to conclusions on fictious test cases and comparing/discussing the results

+ Scheduling auditors to work in pairs for one or more real audits

If used on a regular basis, the last two techniques will maintain the homogeneity between auditors, but they will not prevent the auditor group's judgment from drifting with the passage of time.

Homogeneity in Time

As well as maintaining homogeneity between auditors, detailed audit procedures and methods and adequate supervision of audits can also contribute to the maintenance of consistency over time. Workshops can also contribute if there is a well-documented "solution" to the test cases.

‖ Chapter 8 ‖

Scheduling

Objective

Considering that human resources allocated to internal auditing are often very limited, it is necessary to plan and schedule properly the use of these resources, based on the importance of the activities and processes to be audited.

Approaches

The approach used for scheduling will be a result of the decision on the objectives of the audits program (see chapter 4, paragraph 2). If internal auditors have a mandate to "sweep the floor" before the registrar shows up, then a complete audit—that is, all processes covered by the external standard—will be done one or two months before the external audit.

On the other hand, if internal audits are used as a management tool to measure the processes' compliance and effectiveness, a complete audit can also be done on a regular basis, but it is preferable to perform many partial audits annually. In order to follow this latter approach, the entire QMS has to be split or carved into auditable parts.

Carving of the QMS

The QMS can be split up in many ways. The most frequently used are described in the following paragraphs.

Carving by Concepts/Functions

The QMS can be carved by following functions, each addressing many departments. Most often, these functions are related to clauses of the external standard, such as the following:

1. Training
2. Identification and traceability
3. Documents and data control
4. Corrective and preventive actions

This approach is generally used when a complete internal audit is done in preparation for an external audit.

Carving by Department

The organizational chart can be used to define auditable parts out of departments or sectors. The pieces could be:

1. R&D department
2. Sales department
3. Production department, line # 1
4. Production department, line # 2

This approach has the advantage that, as each piece is directly related to the organization, all audit conclusions in one sector belong to a single manager, who can take corrective action rapidly.

Carving by Process

The QMS can also be carved along the organization's natural processes, such as the following:

1. Sales process
2. Design process
3. Product development process

4. Production equipment purchasing process

5. Raw material procurement process

I strongly recommend this approach for its multiple benefits:

+   It is easy to see the limits of an audit, as each one is directly related to the organization.

+   One round of all the processes is the equivalent of a full system audit.

+   It will detect communication breakdowns between groups, as each process has its suppliers and its customers.

+   It is easier to make a judgment on the effectiveness of the processes, which is normally an important objective of internal quality audits.

Frequency of Audits

Regular Audits

The frequency of audits depends on many factors, the most important being the following:

+   The objectives of the internal audits

+   The audit approach used

+   The method used for carving the QMS

+   The importance of the activities

When complete audits are performed at a regular interval, it is the general understanding that the interval should not exceed 12 months. Internal audits could also be done every 6 or 9 months. If internal audits are done in preparation for the external audits, then the timing of the internal audits is entirely determined by the external audits.

When the QMS is carved along the organization's natural processes, each process can be graded on its importance in relation to the organization's quality objectives. The following is an example of three classes of importance:

A—critical process

B—important process

C—other process

where processes labeled *A* would be audited more often than the *B*s and the *B*s more often than the *C*s. In this example, the interval could be *A*—6 months, *B*—12 months, and *C*—18 months. Once this classification is complete, audits can be scheduled, taking into consideration the other limitations related to availability of resources and technical issues.

This schedule can be documented and maintained by hand, on a form similar to the one shown in Figure 8.1. However, it is perferable to use software on the computer network or on the intranet, so that the audit schedule is readily available to all managers. If the organization has implemented project-planning software, it should be used. In order to obtain a large overview, and especially if some processes are audited every 18 months, the schedule should span at least 24 months and should be updated every 6 months.

For organizations that operate on many shifts, the schedule should include audits during the back shifts. Employees on the evening, night, and weekend shifts are usually the most recently recruited persons, with less experience than those on the day shift.

Unscheduled Audits

In addition to scheduled audits, upper management may trigger ad hoc audits for various reasons, such as the following:

+ A major change in a sector's organization
+ High employee turnover in a department
+ An increase in non-conforming materials or services

It is not presently current practice to trigger an internal audit for a specific need, and this is probably due to internal audits' not yet being perceived as a management tool. As the QMS matures, asking for ad hoc audits may become common

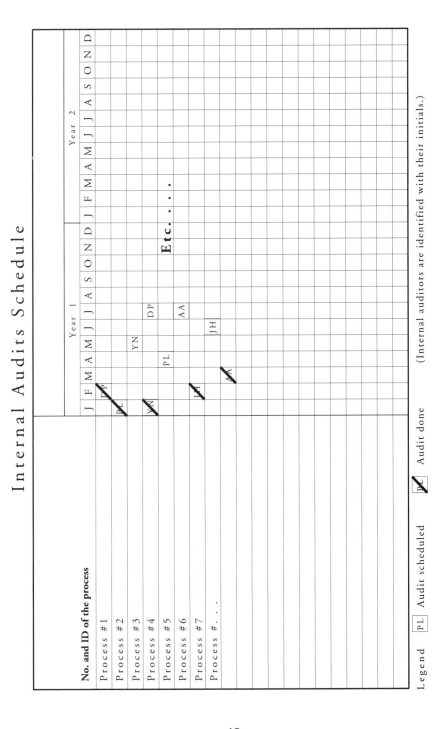

Figure 8.1. Internal audit schedule.

49

practice; in that context, the probability of such audits should be considered when scheduling regular audits and allocating human resources.

External Resources for the Audit

Although most large and medium-size organizations manage and perform their internal audits with internal resources, nothing prevents the use of external human resources for managing or performing the audits.

Managing the Audits

It is rare for an organization to subcontract management of the internal audits program to an external resource. Although not prohibited, it is not practical for most organizations.

Doing the Audits

Some organizations, especially medium-size and small organizations use external auditors, either exclusively or as a complement to their internal auditors team. A unit that is part of a larger organization (a division of a corporation, a service of a government agency) can use auditors from another unit to contribute to internal audits, conversely offering their internal auditors to the other units of the organization. This exchange offers two important benefits:

1. The external auditor brings a fresh, independent look at the audited processes.

2. An important flow of information crosses borders between the two units.

These organizations believe that this cross-pollination and its consequences are worth the extra resources invested in travel time and expenses.

Some small organizations subcontract the performance of all internal audits to external specialists. The associated costs depend on the extent of the audit program, but there is an obvious benefit—not having to worry about or to allocate resources to the qualification of internal auditors.

Are audits still *internal* when done by external resources? Of course. An audit is internal because of its objectives, scope, and methodology—that is, because of its process, which must be defined and approved by the organization's management.

Team Composition
Complete Audits

For complete audits done at a regular interval, a team of a few auditors is needed, the number depending on the size of the organization and on the depth of the audit. At each audit, it may be wise to train one or two new auditors by having them on the team as observers with experienced auditors.

Partial Audits

Each audit is usually done by a single auditor or by a team of two and more rarely by a team of three, depending on circumstances. Auditors-in-training acting as observers are not counted here. Teams of two or three auditors are considered when one or more of the following apply:

1. The processes to be audited require an inquiry of more than two days for a single auditor or more than three days for two auditors.

2. An auditor from another unit of the organization is teamed up with a local auditor.

3. There is a need to maintain or improve homogeneity between internal auditors.

4. The internal audits program is walking through its first steps and the auditors do not feel confident enough to work alone.

| Chapter 9 |

Monitoring the Audit Program

Introduction

Many activities must be accomplished before doing the first audit, as described in previous chapters. We look in this chapter at management activities to be performed continuously to ensure that audit results maintain a high level of adequacy and reliability and to improve the program itself. The level of formalism for these activities depends on the size of the organization and its associated internal audits program.

The audit program and its associated processes also need to be assessed as to whether procedures are adhered to and whether the program delivers sufficient and reliable results. It is not logical to ask the audit process to assess itself, and other methods must be devised.

Audit Supervision

Few Auditors

If the audit program is defined such as to use only a few auditors, then each will be involved in an appreciable number of audit-days every year, thus developing and maintaining their audit skills at a high level. Normal supervision can be limited to the verification of the audit documentation after each audit.

Many Auditors

Occasional auditors need stronger guidelines and better support from a qualified and seasoned auditor. In addition to the verification of audit documents previously described, the program manager can use a combination of the following techniques:

+ Verifying audit documentation at each phase of the audit
+ Helping the audit team for the preparation of each audit
+ Supporting the team when analyzing the observations, in preparation for the closing meeting
+ Being present at the closing meeting
+ Helping write the audit report

Performance Indicators

The performance of an internal audits program depends on the performance of both the auditors and the auditees. Performance indicators, then, should consider these two aspects. To obtain meaningful indicators for a minimal cost, it may be necessary to track scheduling, resources, and audit results with computerized systems. Cost tracking through the accounting system, scheduling with project management software, and using a relational database for audit results are ideal. For audit deficiencies, this database would include:

+ Description of the deviation
+ Major or minor, if a classification is used
+ Compliance- or effectiveness-related, if used
+ Department(s) responsible for the deviation and its correction
+ Topic or subject (use keywords such as *training, documentation, calibration*)
+ Various dates related to the implementation of the corrective action and its follow-up

Auditor Performance

There are no ideal indicators: each organization has to find its own, which depend on its particular objectives and situation. The following indicators should be considered:

+ Use of resources. Upper management will want to know the costs related to internal auditing, as each quantitative output indicator is likely to be put on a ratio to the cost. The cost would include the financial resources needed for training and consultancy, plus the number of persons × days consumed for preparing, doing, and reporting audits, including follow-up audits. Also included could be an estimate of persons × days used for managing the program, supervising auditors as well as scheduling audits. The resulting number of persons × days is then multiplied by the average salary and added to financial expenses on a yearly basis.

+ Time spent on inquiries. Auditors are "productive" in the inquiry phase of the audit, between the opening and closing meetings. The number of persons × days spent inquiring in a given year could be divided by the yearly cost, as previously defined, for the "cost per day of inquiry." The number of persons × days spent for auditors in training (acting as observers in an audit team) should not be included.

+ Commitment of resources. If an organization has difficulty finding time for internal audits, another indicator could be the percentage of audits-days done vs. audits-days scheduled per year. A more stringent indicator would be the percentage of audits done as scheduled— that is, postponed audits being added to canceled audits, as a percentage of audits scheduled.

+ Compliance vs. effectiveness ratio. A mature audit program normally requires that auditors assess both the compliance and the effectiveness of processes. Audit nonconformities could be tagged as being compliance-related or effectiveness-related, with a ratio established between them.

Other indicators—such as the total number of audit nonconformities, either internal or external—are usually not useful indicators. The purpose of the internal audit program is not to raise nonconformities but, rather, to take an accurate picture of the system. And the number of nonconformities raised by the registrar per year is not significant because the number of days spent auditing is so small.

Auditee Performance

The good performance of the auditors is of no value if the auditee does not take adequate, "timely corrective action on deficiencies found during the audit."[1] These two adjectives, *adequate* and *timely,* provide hints to potential indicators:

+ Adequacy. Corrective actions taken by the auditee should be evaluated, in the internal audit program. This is often done by the program manager, as a representative of upper management. Once in a while, a corrective action could be deemed unacceptable because it does not address the real problem. The ratio of unacceptable vs. acceptable corrective action can provide valuable information on whether a given auditee is serious about eliminating causes of problems.

+ Timeliness. With a relational database or a spreadsheet, time-related data on the audit deficiencies over many consecutive audits can be analyzed. All organizations have a few managers showing a level of commitment that is not up to expectations. The worst cases can probably be identified through the eagerness shown (or absence of) in finding solutions to audit findings. This would show as a longer average time taken to decide on and/or implement corrective actions. By carefully measuring and accumulating delays for each position identified as the main actors in corrective actions, factual results will clearly point to managers with a disinclination to quality and auditing. A relational database or spreadsheet can automatically calculate, for each position and problem, the amount of time between the identification of the problem and its correction, and average the result over the number of problems. Minor problems with long delays are a symptom of a lack of commitment in the audit process. Major problems with naturally long delays may be an indication of a lack of commitment to the QMS. Cases of numerous major and minor problems with over-average correction times usually indicate total lack of interest in this "quality fad."

Overall System Performance

The approach of doing many partial audits, no matter how the QMS is carved, carries the risk that the audits will not see problems at the interfaces between the various pieces. Even when carving by business processes, which minimizes this risk, audits may not unearth common mode organizational problems. One way to cover this risk is to use the database to establish strong correlations or recurring topics or departments:

Example 1: Many audits of business processes, done throughout the year, identify among other things a problem related to quality records maintenance—it can reasonably be concluded that the overall control of quality records is not adequate, even without auditing the subject.

Example 2: A Pareto diagram reveals that a large proportion of deviations is related to a single group in the organization—everyone would agree that such a situation needs a closer look.

These correlations constitute factual, indisputable data for management to use in decision making.

Audit Program Review

The audit program should be regularly reviewed for its adequacy and effectiveness, in order to identify opportunities for improvement. In most organizations, this review will be concurrent with the review of the overall QMS. In larger organizations, this may be done independently, and results of the audit program review would be fed to the QMS management review.

Privileged inputs into this audit program review process are the following:

+ Results of audit supervision described previously
+ Performance indicators as previously discussed
+ Results of external audits
+ Reorientation of the organization's policies and objectives
+ Evolving standards related to the QMS or to the audit practices
+ Results of benchmarking with other organizations

Note

1. ISO/DIS 9001:2000.

‖ Chapter 10 ‖

Getting Started

Objective

The way in which an internal audits program is initiated will largely impact on its success. Time and resources must be invested up front to make sure that internal audits are understood and well accepted in the organization.

When?

As discussed in chapter 4, "Objectives and Scope of the Audits Program," it is necessary for a process to be documented before being audited. Then the audits program can start as soon as a few processes have been documented and implemented. In organizations heading for ISO 9000 registration, internal audits are generally initiated halfway through the registration project.

Main Steps

Prerequisite

The resources invested in the program will provide the best payoff when the internal audits are done in a proper environment. The value of audit results has its roots in the information provided by the employees, and, for them to tell auditors what is really going on, management must adopt and put into practice the following principles:

+ Right to mistakes. Upper management must admit that the vast majority of operation mistakes have their causes outside of the person making the mistake and that the purpose of internal audits is to identify the causes or conditions leading to errors.
+ Respect for the individual. Employees are neither capricious celebrities nor automatons. Each individual has the responsibility to learn what is needed to do his or her work, as well as the right to access to all necessary information and training, including learning from mistakes.

These two principles call for a transparent management style, an openness in which management decisions and results are accessible and therefore subject to criticism.

Identification of a Project Manager

A person that will drive the implementation should be found, and that person trained in the internal audits concepts. The required training will depend on the person's background—the person should possess all skills and knowledge necessary to do audits and to define, implement, and manage the program.

Information to Upper Management

Upper management—that is, the customer of the process—should be made aware of how internal audits can contribute to the decision-making processes by providing pertinent information on business processes. This explanation should be made in a formal session, maybe a half-day, in which the "foundations of the program" will also be decided.

Foundations of the Program

Upper management must decide on the objectives and scope of the program, necessary human resources and their associated qualifications, and the approach for scheduling. The project manager can then produce a first draft of the audit procedure and have it approved by upper management.

Information to Middle Management

If the organization is large enough to have many middle managers, sufficient time must be taken to "sell" internal audits, to explain how internal audits *will contribute* to management decisions, using the approved draft audit procedure as a supporting document. Managers should be reassured that the internal audits will attempt to find flaws in the QMS, and not hunt for culprits or scapegoats.

Appointment of a Program Manager

Before or after the middle management awareness session(s), the person who will eventually manage the audits program must be identified and trained. This step is not required if, as in most cases, the project manager will also be the program manager.

Auditor Selection and Training

See chapter 6, "Auditor Qualification and Competence."

Practice Audit

The first audit should be a "dummy" audit, to familiarize both auditors and auditees with the audit process and methods. By specifying that the audit results will not be used (that is, there are no consequences to the audit), the auditors do not feel pressure to be adequate and the auditees do not fear the consequences. After this audit, the audit team and auditees should be debriefed, with the objective of learning and improving the audit process.

Audit Procedure

After the practice audit has been debriefed, the audit procedure will likely need some adjustments. If some changes impact on the program foundations, it should be verified with upper management that these changes are acceptable, then the first official version of the audit procedure can be produced.

Program Launch

A first audit schedule should be drafted, keeping it light. If the organization is heading towards ISO 9000 registration, the audit schedule should cover all activities at least once before the registration audit. External resources may be useful here because both the number of audits and the number of corrective actions may be significantly higher at this point than what will be experienced at "cruising speed." The organization should be informed with the distribution of the audit procedure and first audit schedule.

Section Two

Doing an Audit

| Chapter 11 |

Introduction

This section is intended for persons who are assigned the task of doing an internal audit, either alone or as a team leader. Persons having to participate as a member of an audit team would benefit in reading the chapters on audit preparation and on inquiry.

Activities described in this section will span no more than a few weeks and in some cases will take only a few days. The activities start when the auditor or team leader initiates the preparation and finish when the audit report is issued. For reasons of convenience, this section also includes a chapter on follow-up audits.

When an auditor or a team leader accepts an audit mandate, the audit program manager has already made some decisions that, in an external audit, are usually made during the preparation phase:

+ Objective of the audit
+ Scope of audited processes
+ Team composition
+ Date brackets

In some organizations, especially when internal quality auditors are regular employees, the audit program manager will also do some of the activities described in this section. The intent is to minimize the amount of time the auditor spends auditing, away from the regular job. Typical examples are the audit plan and the audit notification to the auditee(s). It is therefore critical for the auditor or team leader to know exactly where to start.

‖ Chapter 12 ‖

Basic Concepts

An Audit

What is this "internal quality audit" that has to be done? An audit is a verification exercise to confirm that something is correct. We can compare an audit to the 30,000 mi check-up on a car: the mechanic does a systematic verification of lubricants, ball joints, drive train, cooling system, and so

> Audit: systematic, independent and documented process for obtaining evidence and evaluating it objectively to determine the extent to which audit criteria are fulfilled.[1]
>
> ISO/CD1 19011 §3.1

on following a predefined checklist, in order to confirm that everything is correct. Cars being imperfect, it is likely that minor corrections will be needed for another trouble-free 30,000 mi.

Similarly in an audit, after having gone through a pre-established list of verifications, it is likely that the auditor will identify minor or

> Unlike the auto mechanic, the auditor does not take any part in the corrections.

major "repairs." It is part of the job, although not the purpose of the audit. The quality of an auditor is not measured by the number of repairs, but by the adequacy of the diagnostic.

A Quality Audit

A "quality audit" is a verification of the aspects of the organization that are related to the quality of the material and services produced. These aspects are traditionally presented in three levels, as in Figure 12.1:

1. Management processes, such as the training of personnel and the solution of internal problems
2. Realization processes, which can be subdivided:
   + Information-related processes, such as the design and the purchase of raw materials
   + Physical transformation processes, such as the mixing of products, metal bending, and food preparation.
3. Results delivered to the customers

This model is much used in organizations that transform material as their main business, but it can hardly be used in service organizations. On the other hand, we generally label as "service" results which contain both:

1. A material, tangible component which can be considered independently from the service delivery, (such as the food in a restaurant and the blank checks of a banking institution); this component is easily measurable

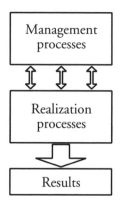

Figure 12.1. Traditional model for an organization.

2. An intangible component, closely connected to the delivery process itself (employee politeness, orchestra performance at the concert); for this component, quality is not judged on the delivery process parameters but, rather, on the customer perception with respect to expectations, precisely at that moment

A more generic model is proposed in Figure 12.2 that includes intangible as well as tangible components, which could apply to all organizations. It is now generally accepted that all organizations produce a combination of tangible and intangible components, in a variable percentage. Keeping the concept of three levels, we have:

1. The same management processes
2. Realization processes that will ultimately deliver the results:
   + Processes that transform information internally, such as the design and the purchase of raw materials
   + On one side, processes that transform material (such as mixing products, bending metal, and cooking food) and

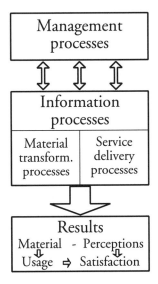

Figure 12.2. Proposed model for an organization.

on the other side, delivery processes in contact with the customer

3. Tangible and intangible results

The audit techniques can be applied to each of the three levels. Let's examine what this entails.

Auditing the Results

A result audit, better known as a product audit, is a verification of all the characteristics and functions of a product as acquired by a customer, with reference to the planned functions and designed characteristics. This operation must be prepared carefully to limit verification to the functions and characteristics that have an impact on the overall quality of the product. For example, for a home toaster the following could be verified:

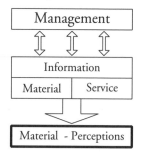

Figure 12.3. Auditing results.

+ Performance. Does it toast evenly, in the specified time, and so on?

+ Maintenance. Is it easy to clean, safe, and so on?

+ Internal characteristics. What are the temperature of the heating elements, wall thickness, gauge of electric wires, resistance of external finish, solidity of welded joints, and so on?

Audit results are generally expressed, for the more complex products, in defects per million. Often called a "product audit," this consumes a lot of resources even for a single product and therefore is not generally used by small and medium-size companies.

The idea of auditing results is not applicable to customer perceptions, which are intangible results. To evaluate customer perceptions, an organization must use tried and validated survey techniques, by measuring a statistically valid sample rather than a unique object.

Auditing Realization Processes

A process audit is a verification that a realization process follows the planned arrangements, for which it can be verified *how* activities are done (the method) and their *results*. As this is a critical concept, a few examples may clarify it.

As a first example, let's examine the hot bonding of two pieces of wood, in the manufacture of furniture. Among other things, the verification would cover:

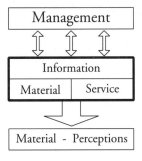

+ Method. Are the amount and temperature of glue, drying time, temperature and pressure, and so on conforming to the procedure?

Figure 12.4. Auditing processes.

+ Results. Does the resistance to pull and shear meets specifications?

As a second example, let's examine the purchasing of raw material for the previous example. Among other things, the verification would cover:

+ Method. Are specifications approved; are purchase orders complete, approved, issued; and so on?

+ Results. Are wood and glue available for production, in appropriate quantity, when and where required, and so on?

As a third example, let's examine a three-day internal auditor training course. The verification would probably cover:

+ Method. Is the agenda followed as specified; is the training place comfortable; is all required training material available, and so on?

✦ Results. Have the participants acquired the necessary skills and knowledge?

It is important that both the method and the results be verified. If only the results are verified, it can be determined whether they are adequate, but not whether they are due to luck or to a systematic process. If an adequate result is due to good luck, how much confidence can be placed in results that are not verified? The added verification and confirmation that a process is defined and followed provide confidence that results are consistent.

Besides, if only the compliance of activities to the defined method is verified, appropriate confidence is gained that the results are consistent, without knowing if they are adequate. Unless an organization wants to deploy "random management," it is necessary to verify and confirm *compliance of activities to planned arrangements* and *conformance of results to specifications*.

Auditing Management Processes

Auditing management processes is a different situation because it deals with activities that do not produce tangible results. It is important to have a good grasp of what the activities are before attempting to audit them. The following short list of management processes will clarify these activities:

✦ Defining quality policies and objectives, as well as updating them as needed

✦ Planning strategies for the implementation of the policies and of subsequent changes

✦ Defining a structure, assigning responsibilities, allocating necessary resources, and updating them as needed

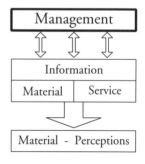

Figure 12.5. Auditing management.

✦ Deploying human resources, including hiring, training, career planning, and so on

✦ Deploying realization (production) and measuring equipment

✦ Managing the flow of information and data, from management to employees for direction and support, as well as from employees to management for decisions based on factual information

✦ Controlling problem areas, such as customer complaints and excessive downtime

✦ Running a continuous improvement process, both in reactive and preventive modes

Expected results from these and other management processes cannot be expressed in terms of measurable specifications. Most of these processes will be described in procedures, each ideally containing the purpose/objective of the concerned process. Although these processes may be more difficult to audit, it is important that the audit both verifies that the activities are performed and assesses the achievement of expected results.

Groups and Actors in an Audit

The historical context of auditing has resulted in the use of three terms related to persons or groups of persons for all audits:

✦ Client: any organization that requests the audit; specifies the objective, scope, and reference standards; and uses

> Client: organization or person requesting an audit.
>
> ISO/CD1 19011:2001

the audit results in its decision-making processes. For an internal quality audit, the organization's management is the client.

✦ Auditing organization: a group responsible for conducting the verification and for reporting the conclusions to

> Auditor: person qualified to conduct audits.
>
> ISO/CD1 19011:2001

the client. This auditing organization employs persons that will accomplish the tasks, and these persons are generally called "auditors" (see the section "Audit Team Composition"). In internal audits, this auditing organization is headed by the person who manages the internal quality audits. This person can also act as an auditor, while employing other persons from within or outside the organization.

✦ Audited organization: also called the "auditee," the group whose processes are subject to the audit. It can be

> Auditee: organization being audited.
>
> ISO/CD1 19011:2001

a department, a plant, a division, or even a multiple-unit organization. In an internal audit, frequently the person in charge of the auditee, as part of management, is also a client of the audit conclusions.

Three Types of Quality Audits

Three types of quality audits can be distinguished, based on the relationships among client, auditor, and auditee.

When an organization does a self-verification on the operation and effectiveness of its quality system, that is a "first-party audit," or internal audit. In this type of audit, the separation among client, auditor, and auditee is blurred (see Figure 12.6), since the same person can play each of these roles at different times.

Figure 12.6. First-party audit.

An organization can audit a supplier in order to increase its confidence that the supplier has planned the quality-related activities and that the supplier follows the planning. Such a supplier audit is also called a "second-party audit" (see Figure 12.7). For decades, it was the only type of audit in use, and the auditing tools and techniques, as well as the desirable auditor behavior, were defined in that environment.

Figure 12.7. Second-party audit.

The quality audit practice is now largely used in "third-party audits," in which the QMS of an organization is formally recognized by an external and independent agency (see Figure 12.8). Any organization that wishes to publicize how good its QMS is will use the services of a registration agency, or registrar. This registrar will verify that some qual-

Figure 12.8. Third-party audit.

ity-related activities are planned and done and that the QMS delivers materials and services that meet customer needs. This is also called a "registration audit" and sometimes a "certification audit."

These three basic types of audits are completed with many variations. The better known is a quality audit done by the head office of an organization, of one division, in order to confirm that it meets a corporate quality directive.

Although known and occasionally done as early as 1980, internal quality audits and registration audits spread quickly in the early 1990s, when the ISO 9000 family of standards was adopted by a large number of organizations. By 1990, the vast majority of auditors had learned how to audit in supplier audits. Since then, the audit methods have evolved and have been adapted to the two other types of audits.

Audit Reference Documents

Auditing being a verification activity, the need for objectivity calls for documented reference(s). The absence of such reference(s) leaves a door wide open to unreasonable, and even abusive, conclusions. Many documents can be used as audit references, depending on what is audited.

Product Audit

For the functional verification, the marketing briefs and product concept descriptions are used. For the technical characteristics, the verification relies on drawings and specifications resulting from the design process. If applicable, laws and regulations are used for both functional and technical verification.

Transformation and Delivery Processes Audit

For verification of compliance, the audit references are either standardized methods (international- national-, or sector-specific) or methods developed internally. For verification of results, the audit uses internal specifications related to in-process products and service delivery.

Information and Management Processes Audit

Audit references are quality-related standards, as well as procedures implemented in the organization within the QMS. Quality-related standards could be management guidelines such as ISO 9004, the Malcolm Baldrige criteria, or the Canada Awards for Excellence criteria. They could also be management requirements such as ISO 9001, QS-9000, or ISO 13485, which can be required by customers or regulatory agencies.

Objectives and Scope of an Internal Quality Audit

An internal quality audit can have many interrelated objectives, and the scope can be as small as a single activity or as large as the overall quality management system.

Scope of the Overall Audit Program

Two types of audit scope can be defined in an organization:

1. The audit program can be limited to the QMS activities that are directly related to the external quality requirements, such as ISO 9001 or QS-9000.

2. The audit program can cover all the QMS activities, including those not covered by an external standard, such as cost of quality and process/product improvement.

Frequency of Audits

It is generally accepted that the interval between two consecutive audits of a given process is one year, but other approaches are also possible. Two models for scheduling audits have emerged:

1. The organization does a quality audit of the entire scope, at a fixed interval varying from 6 to 12 months; this model has the great advantage of simplicity.

2. The organization separates the overall scope into smaller segments, auditing each at a different time of the year. This model offers the flexibility of assigning a different frequency to each segment and selecting an appropriate timing for the audits. This frequency depends on the importance of the activities in the segment. An annual schedule would look like the example in Figure 12.9. When this model is used, the overall program is usually carved along the lines of business processes.

The audit program manager is responsible for having the approach and model decided by management. As that is done

Segments	J	F	M	A	M	J	J	A	S	O	N	D
Segment #1	▓											
Segment #2*			▓					▓				
Segment #3**							▓					
Segment #4		▓										
Segment #5					▓							
Etc. . . .												

* = Important activities audited every six months
** = Activities more easily audited during the summer, for example

Figure 12.9. Part of an annual schedule.

early in the implementation process, the audit program manager can inform the audit team leader of the objectives and scope of each audit.

Objectives of Internal Quality Audits

Thus, auditing is essentially a verification activity. The auditor or audit team is asked to make a judgment—but on what?

- ✦ Compliance. Activities to be performed in the organization are planned, and the planning is often written in a paper document or computer file. After having gathered the information, the auditor should be able to answer the following questions: Are actual activities in compliance with what was planned and documented (see Figure 12.10)? If not, what is the difference?
- ✦ Effectiveness. Activities are structured in a process in order to provide measurable results. Some results are

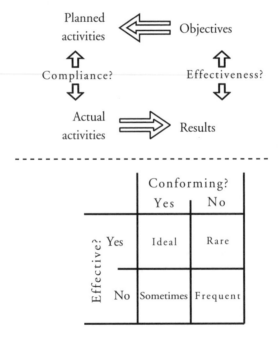

Figure 12.10. Compliance and effectiveness of processes.

information-based, such as drawings and specifications' being the output of the design process. Other results are material-based, such as in a production facility. Finally, results can also be service-based, such as the training of personnel. After collecting data, the auditor should be able to answer the following questions: Is the audited process delivering the results it was set up for? If not, what is the shortcoming?

+ Efficiency. There are many ways to achieve a given result, and each uses a certain amount of resources (personnel, equipment, space, and so on). When the organization defined its QMS, managers had to select one of the many possible ways to have a system of interconnected processes. Pushing into this area, the auditor must answer: Is the process efficient? Is it the way that uses the least amount of resources? If not, what would be a better way?

Auditors are very rarely asked to judge process efficiency; internal or external quality audits are limited to compliance and effectiveness. These two objectives have to be considered together. That the activities be compliant and the process effective is certainly the goal of the organization, but auditors often see other situations (refer to Figure 12.10):

+ The activities are done as planned, but the process does not fully deliver all expected results.
+ The process is effective in delivering the results, although the activities are different from what was planned.
+ Activities are not complying with planning, *and* proper results are not delivered.

Audit Team Composition

For an audit of limited scope and time, a single auditor can be responsible for the whole audit and perform all the required activities. For a larger audit, a team of persons with various qualifications is assembled. Members of the team have specific roles, each traditionally associated with responsibilities and activities. It is always possible, in a given team, to modify the responsibilities and activities of each member. The following are traditional roles:

+ Team leader. Person responsible for the entire audit, which includes leading the audit team. The tasks include:
  1. Acquire resources that are needed to perform all activities required by the audit scope
  2. Discharge work to the team members, taking into consideration each member's qualifications
  3. Supervise the audit activities and monitor the audit progress
  4. Maintain communication among team members, as well as with the client (audit program manager) and the auditee

+ Auditor. Person responsible for performing the assigned audit tasks, such as the preparation of working documents, inquiry, and audit report, which is described in chapter 13.

+ Observer. Person having no responsibility in achieving audit results, although the observer may be asked to perform some actions. An audit team may have an observer for one of the following reasons:
  1. As an auditor-in-training, in the early stages of the qualification process; on a given audit, the observer can follow more than one auditor
  2. As a senior auditor in the auditing organization, assessing the performance of one or more members of the audit team
  3. As a client representative in a second-party audit, evaluating the auditing organization's resources and methods

+ Specialist. Person having an excellent technical knowledge of the audited sector. This person is responsible for supporting the auditors and team leader in understanding the relevance and impact of audit observations. An internal audit team generally does not need access to a specialist because the auditors are familiar with the organization's activities. A specialist may be useful in a second-party audit; however, specialists are used mostly in registration audits, when a registrar does not have auditors qualified for a specific sector of activities.

It is possible for one member of the team to act in more than one capacity. Frequently, the team leader also acts as an auditor. One of the auditors can also be a specialist, supporting the other team members. At the other extreme, it is obviously not possible for an auditor-in-training to act as a team leader.

Audit Phases

The internal quality audit program is composed of many activities, as shown in a wheel model in Figure 12.11. This model is useful in showing that:

+ The overall program is made up of interrelated processes.
+ Each audit is a sequence of three processes—preparation, inquiry, and report.

Figure 12.11. Audit wheel model.

- The program management, which includes the selection and qualification of auditors, is a critical activity because it is the basis of all other activities.

- The credibility of audit results is determined mostly by the competence of the auditors.

- A documented method is necessary to ensure consistency between auditors, to ensure consistency over time, and to ensure that the audit processes are effectively interconnected.

Note

1. A shorter, better definition would be: "process for obtaining evidence and evaluating it objectively to determine the extent to which audit criteria are fulfilled."

| Chapter 13 |

Planning for the Inquiry

Duration

The planning phase starts when the assigned team leader initiates the activities. It ends before the meeting that triggers the on-site inquiry. It is the first of the three phases, planning, inquiry, and report, that make a typical internal audit (see Figure 13.1). The planning activities can take many weeks, or maybe only a few days, depending on how the organization has defined its audit process. If the planning includes all the activities described in this chapter, this phase should be started approximately four weeks prior to the expected inquiry dates.

Purpose of the Planning

All the activities that are done before the inquiry, including even auditor training and audit scheduling, ensure that:

1. The inquiry will be conducted rapidly, and at the right moment, in order to minimize the inconvenience for the auditee.

2. Enough information will be collected in the imparted time frame, in order to draw valid conclusions.

3. The auditors can collect pertinent information, analyze it and come to conclusions that are useful for all involved—in particular, for the audited units and the management.

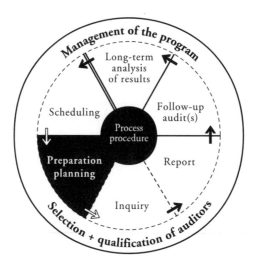

Figure 13.1. Planning phase in model.

Resources

All the planning activities described here must be performed, and at the right moment. Otherwise, parts of the inquiry will have to be improvised, and the validity of the audit results could suffer.

All these activities may have to be carried out by the audit team members assigned to the audit, or some may have already been done by the program manager in an effort to reduce the auditor's workload. Which activities are done by the manager, and which are carried out by the audit team are defined in the audit process procedure—this procedure should be consulted early in the planning phase.

Inputs

For best results, the audit program should allow for the following inputs to be available, at a minimum:

+ Identification of the team leader or of the unique auditor
+ Audit objectives
+ Audit criteria

+ Audit scope—that is, the processes to be audited
+ Bracket of dates for the inquiry
+ Documents describing the processes to be audited

The auditors should also have access to internal and external audit reports related to the audited processes, as well as to findings from previous audits.

If the audit program manager has performed some of the planning activities beforehand, other inputs will be available, such as:

+ Precise dates for the inquiry
+ Identification of all team members
+ Documents required for the inquiry

The following paragraphs cover all the activities normally required at the planning stage, regardless of who performs them.

Outputs

At the end of this phase, the audit team should have:

+ A document describing the audit objectives and scope
+ The audit team composition and the exact inquiry dates
+ The identification and availability of all necessary reference documents, such as process documentation, internal and external standards, and the organization's general objectives as well as quality objectives
+ Working documents, often called "audit checklists"
+ A schedule of the activities during the inquiry, which will enable the auditee to coordinate the availability of personnel
+ An agenda for the opening meeting, if such a meeting is held

In addition to these documents, each auditor will have become prepared on how to interface with the auditee personnel.

Audit Feasibility

The very first task of the team leader is to question the feasibility of the audit:

1. Are audit objectives, criteria, and scope clear and well defined ? Internal audits are often done without clear criteria, especially those criteria related to effectiveness. What are the expected outputs of each process that has to be audited? Ideally, the expected outputs of a process are found in the "Purpose" section of the process procedure itself. But, quite often, the "Purpose" just says: "The purpose of this procedure is to describe the XYZ process." If criteria are not available, then they will have to be defined as part of the audit preparation.

2. Are allocated resources sufficient to achieve the audit objectives for the specified scope? Are there enough auditors and enough time to prepare, inquire into, and report on all activities and locations covered in the audit scope?

Audit Team vs. Duration of the Inquiry

The second task of the team leader is to select the members of the audit team and to decide on the duration of the inquiry. In many internal audits programs, this is decided beforehand by the program manager and is available as an input to the planning phase.

The audit team rarely includes a specialist for an internal audit. However, there might be observers, such as auditors-in-training.

The number and type of auditors required and the duration of the inquiry are a function of the audit objectives (compliance/effectiveness/efficiency), of the audit scope (how many processes), and of the nature and extent of the processes under audit. "Extent" is the number of employees involved and the physical area to be covered during the inquiry. "Nature" means that the necessary auditor competence is different when auditing the design process from the storage/delivery process.

When assembling the audit team, the team leader has to consider that each auditor must be independent of the process under audit. Each auditor must be free of any bias, positive or negative, toward the audited process and the personnel involved in the audited process. This independence has two components:

> Some organizations use teams of two auditors working together, one independent and the other from the audited unit; the independent auditor has the responsibility for the team. In the same audit, the team responsibility can shift from one to the other as the team moves from one department to another.

1. The auditor has not been involved in the audited process or in the unit that owns the process for some years.

2. The auditor does not have an emotional relationship with any of the personnel in the audited unit (through family or other ties).

All decisions related to the number of auditors, the duration of the inquiry, and the selection of audit team members should be made in consultation with the audit program manager, who reports to upper management on the amount of resources used annually for internal quality audits.

Initial Contacts

Early in the planning phase, the team leader should contact each manager of the units that will be audited. This initial contact aims at:

+ Confirming the objectives and scope of the audit. It is true that managers should have agreed on the annual audit schedule; however, many will have forgotten because internal auditing is not a frequent activity, and is often perceived as a less-important activity as well.

+ Deciding on exact dates. First the programmed bracket of dates must be confirmed as still valid, and, if so, dates for the inquiry are selected; otherwise, the matter must be taken for resolution to the audit program manager.

+ Confirming the use of auditors. Once the dates have been finalized, it is important to confirm the availability of human resources, with the unit manager each auditor comes from.

+ Validating the team. The audited units must be informed on which auditors will make up the team, so that they have an opportunity to express any concern relative to their independence.

Reference Documents

The team leader should list all documents (including computer files) that could be useful when analyzing the audit data and when coming to audit conclusions. Two types of documents can be defined, based on their usage:

1. Process-related documents: any document or computer file describing the process, such as the quality manual, system procedures, work instructions, forms and others. At least the quality manual and the system procedures should be close at hand when planning the audit.

2. Other documents: any documents that are not directly connected to the processes but that can have a direct impact on the organization. These can be standards (ISO 9001, corporate standards, and so on) or government regulations that apply to the sector (food, medical, public transportation, and so on). The auditors must have an adequate understanding of these requirements—it is not necessary to carry a copy into the inquiry, but the auditors should know where to get a copy if the need arises.

Team Set-Up

If there is more than one auditor, the team leader assigns audited processes to each auditor. In doing this, the team leader must take a lighter load, because he or she will need time for coordination and communication. If the audit team is composed of two or three members, as is often the case for internal audits, the team leader can take a significant part of the audit work. In a large internal audit, with an important team, the coordination and communication activities are likely to occupy the team leader full-time.

A table for the assignment of processes to auditors can be used, ensuring that everything is covered and that all auditors have a fairly balanced workload. An example of a task allocation form is shown in Figure 13.2. This table can also be kept as a model in a spreadsheet, where all processes are listed with their corresponding workloads.

When the audited processes have been assigned, the team leader normally calls a team meeting, where he or she:

+ Clarifies the audit objectives and scope
+ Describes the allocation of tasks
+ Confirms that all auditors understand their responsibilities and have the necessary resources
+ Validates that all auditors are independent from the audited processes and units
+ Provides general information, such as dates and places for the audit

This team meeting can also be a good occasion to refresh the auditors' knowledge of audited processes, of audit forms to be used, and of interviewing techniques.

Schedule of Inquiry Activities

Once the audited units have accepted the selection of auditors, and knowing that each auditor feels independent of the assigned processes, the team leader then produces a schedule detailing the sequence of activities for each auditor, for each day. This schedule should have an accuracy of ± ¼ of a day, or ± ¼ of a work shift. Figure 13.3 shows a sample schedule of activities for a team of two auditors over two days. This schedule has a three-fold purpose:

Organization

Tasks allocation

Audit: _____

Date(s): _____

Processes under audit	Approx. load (hours)	Team leader	Peter	John	Paul
Reception and storage of goods	3	3			
Calibration of scales	2			2	
Preventive maintenance program	4				4
Internal transportation and handling	1	1			
Training	1			1	
Etc.....	4			4	
	2				2
	4		4		
	3		3		
	1				1
Total hours	25	4	7	7	7

Form #, revision #

Figure 13.2. Task allocation form.

ABC   **Schedule of activities**
Food Store   Audit #: 97-C-2
                                         Date(s): March 12/13

	Mary	Jane
	08:00: Opening meeting	08:00: Opening meeting
A.M.	Meat preparation Seafood preparation Cheese preparation	Procurement Receiving/identification Handling - storage
P.M.	Maintenance of the fruit display Maintenance of the vegetables display Maintenance of the dairy products display	Preventive maintenance program Calibration of scales External building maintenance
Evening	Maintenance of the fruit display Maintenance of the vegetables display Maintenance of the dairy products display Closing of the computer systems	Customer complaints Cash deposits process General cleaning process
A.M.	Bread and pastry kitchen Qualification of personnel	Customer complaints Cash deposits process Bar coding system Control of documents and records
P.M.	Analysis of audit evidence and findings Closing meeting	

Form #, revision #

Figure 13.3. Schedule of activities for an inquiry.

1. The team leader confirms that all the processes included in the audit scope have been covered.

2. The manager of each audited unit can identify persons that will be needed for the audit.

3. The team leader will use it to reassign tasks during the inquiry, as necessary.

Each audit team member is given a copy of the schedule. If the objective and scope of the audit are such that a single auditor does the inquiry in half a day, then a formal schedule is not useful.

Audit Notification

All the preceding activities help clarify the need for personnel, the allocation of time, and the necessary documentation. They culminate in the written confirmation of all the elements that surround the inquiry. This document is copied to the persons responsible for the audited organizational units, hence the term *audit notification.*

This audit notification (see Figure 13.4) usually contains two elements:

1. A simple form containing:
   - ✦ Audit objectives
   - ✦ Audit scope
   - ✦ Involved organizational units
   - ✦ Processes under audit
   - ✦ Reference documents
   - ✦ Members of the audit team, including any observers
   - ✦ Dates and times
2. The schedule of inquiry activities described in the previous section of this chapter.

For smaller audits—for example, when a single auditor verifies a few processes in one day or less—the audit notification can be limited to a single page that also contains the schedule of activities. A simplified version of an audit notification is shown in Figure 13.5.

ABC
Food Store

A u d i t   n o t i f i c a t i o n

Audit #: 99-C-1

Auditee: all departments _____
Copies: store manager _____
            head of departments _____

Audited procedure: all procedures in force at time of audit _____
References: quality manual: edition # 1.1 _____

Auditor(s): Mary and Jane _____
Date(s): March 11 and 12, 20XX _____

Comments:

1) First complete internal audit, prior to the registration audit;

2) An external resource will be available to guide the two auditors; this external resource will not actively participate in the audit;

3) Corrective actions will not be raised; results will be used to identify the areas that still need improvement;

4) See the attached schedule of activities.

Par: ____Mary_____   Date: ____February 12____

Figure 13.4. Audit notification form.

ABC   A u d i t   n o t i f i c a t i o n
Food Store   (s i m p l i f i e d)

Audit #: 00-C-2

Auditee: reception of goods and merchandise   _____

Copies: store manager   _____

      quality manager   _____

Audited procedure: QSP-05 receiving and storage   _____

References: quality manual: chapter 5, edition #2.1   _____

Auditor(s): Jane   _____

Date(s): March 10, 20XX   _____

Comments:

1) Carl is being trained as an auditor—he will participate as an observer.

Schedule of activities:

Inquiry will start 08:00—no opening meeting.

Reception and identification of received goods
Verification of goods
Handling and internal transportation
Storage (including HACCP requirements)
Maintenance of storage areas
Related documents and records

Closing meeting—3 P.M., unless otherwise indicated

_____

_____

_____

Par: _____*Jane*_____ Date: _____February 11_____

Figure 13.5. Simplified audit notification form.

The audit notification is copied to all persons who need the information, normally, the following:

+ Members of the audit team
+ Audited organizational units
+ Manager of the internal audits program

This audit notification can be sent by e-mail without using paper form, if this technique is available.

Audit Checklist

Each auditor must have a working document that will help in:

+ Preparing the inquiry
+ Understanding the processes under audit
+ Preparing the logistical aspects
+ Ensuring that everything is covered in the audit
+ Documenting observations and personal notes during the inquiry

Although commonly called a "checklist," it is certainly not a yes/no checklist or an equivalent of an inspection checklist. In order to be useful, this document must, either by itself or in conjunction with process documents:

+ Clearly describe the audited process, highlighting the purpose of the process.
+ Identify which activities will be examined, through questions, statements, or visually highlighted keywords in a document.
+ Use a format that will leave plenty of room for jotting down notes, observations, and supplementary questions for the inquiry.

There is no standard format for the audit checklist—the format used will depend on the audit objectives and on whether a permanent or temporary document is needed.

Audit Objective: Compliance to ISO 9001

In this case, seasoned auditors can use a generic checklist containing all the elements of the ISO 9001 standard, such as the type of document used by registrar auditors. This checklist is a profitable solution, since copies are available at a reasonable cost, although its use requires very skilled auditors.

This approach is often used to measure the progress of the ISO 9000 implementation project, often using external auditors:

+ Initially for a diagnostic of the quality management system in reference to ISO 9001
+ One or more times to measure the implementation progress
+ Finally for the first internal quality audit, before the registration audit

Once the quality management system has been registered, I recommend an approach focused on the organization's own processes.

Audit Objective: Compliance of Activities and Effectiveness of Processes

Permanent Checklist

It is possible to create a simple, permanent checklist for each process, to be used in conjunction with the procedure. It will do the following:

+ Clearly describe the process objectives.
+ Identify all the activities to be verified, with a reference to the procedure.
+ List the forms and the work instructions related to the process.

With plenty of blank space on the checklist, auditors can add questions or comments while preparing for the inquiry. This approach is much used and very valuable because it ensures a good coverage of the audit scope and better consistency between auditors, even with a less experienced auditor. But it comes with a price: a large amount of resources are needed up front for creating a checklist for each process, as well as continual resources for updating checklists as process procedures are revised.

Specific Checklist

It is also possible to create a checklist every time an audit is performed. Though this would be very effective in preparing for the inquiry, it would consume a lot of time, and most organizations turn to other solutions.

I recommend using the procedure itself as the starting point for the checklist, printed single-sided. During the preparation, the auditor can use an appropriate pen to highlight the process objectives and the keywords pointing to important activities. The back side can then be used to add supplementary questions or comments, and that is where the auditor will document the observations and notes during the inquiry.

If the procedure is available in electronic format, it may be easier to create a new document for each audit by:

+ Changing from the "portrait" to the "landscape" mode (usually done in <page format> menu), assigning a 10 cm right margin to the text (see Figure 13.6); if already in "portrait" mode, just modify the right margin

Figure 13.6. From portrait to landscape.

✦ Eliminating elements of the procedure that are related to its control, such as title page, signatures, revision list, and distribution

✦ Eliminating or reducing the size of any text that does not describe activities

✦ Highlighting keywords and sentences

The big advantage of using the procedure itself as the starting point of the checklist for each audit is that one knows for sure that the checklist is up-to-date. With a minimum of word-processing skills, an auditor can make these transformations while performing the next activity—that is, gaining a good knowledge of the process.

One word of caution is needed when working with procedures which do not describe the process purpose. Time has to be invested, then, to define criteria needed to determine effectiveness and to have these criteria accepted by the auditee and client.

Understanding of the Process

The auditor must have a good understanding of the audited processes before showing up for the inquiry. The auditor needs not be a specialist—this could even be a handicap—but a basic knowledge will help in distinguishing important activities from less important ones. This knowledge can be acquired through a combination of the following:

✦ Creating a specific checklist

✦ Carefully reading the procedure and related documents

✦ Having worked in the same or similar processes

✦ Listening to explanations from competent persons

This knowledge is essential in order to collect meaningful data and to come to valid conclusions on the compliance and effectiveness of the audited processes.

Personal Preparation

When preparing for an audit, an auditor naturally covers the technical aspects described in the previous pages but often forgets to prepare for the emotional aspects of the audit. An inquiry is always an inquiry and is usually intimidating, with its load of stress and anxiety. Each auditor must collect a lot of pertinent information in a minimal amount of time, through interpersonal relationships that have an emotional as well as a technical component.

It is often believed that an internal audit is easier and more relaxed than an external audit. On the contrary, the auditor and the interviewed personnel share a company culture, and they already have a perception of each other, even before the audit is scheduled. And they will continue to work in the same organization after the audit. This imposes on an internal auditor some concerns that go far beyond the success of the audit itself.

Unless an internal auditor is very experienced, which is not common for an internal auditor, that person should spend some time preparing for effective communication. But how?

There is no magic method. By analyzing the information contained in the audit schedule, an auditor can foresee and prepare for possible events. Table 13.1 lists a few examples.

An auditor should also consider how the personnel perceive audits. It may be that the organization has experienced difficult or bad external audits. It could be that the personnel do not perceive the value of internal audits. This should also be addressed with a simple explanation in order to obtain the cooperation of the interviewees.

Remember that each person in an audit will, in the first minute of the encounter, forge an image of the auditor. It is important to prepare for this initial contact. An often used technique is to visualize this first contact, that is, imagine yourself in the situation, before the audit, for various potential circumstances.

If one interviewee does not know what an audit is, how can it be explained in one minute?	Prepare an opener that includes: ✦ You work for the same organization. ✦ You are not assessing the person or the position. ✦ The purpose is to assess how the organization operates. ✦ The report will not mention names.
How do I tell the interviewee what I am looking for?	Prepare an introduction in which you clarify: ✦ What is the audited process. ✦ Which information and data you need for the audit.

(Example for a buyer: "This morning, we are looking at the procurement process, and I would like to know on what basis you qualify and assess our suppliers.")

How do I approach a person whose rank is much higher than mine?	Prepare questions in terms of activities and measurable results.

(Example: You interview a vice president on design control :
* *"How is each design project planned?"*

* *"Is this planning documented? [if yes] Can I see a sample?"*

* *"What are the sources of the design input data? How are these data documented? Can I see a sample? Have they been verified, and by whom? How is this verification recorded?")*

Other events are foreseeable—take time to state these events and to seek help on how to address them.

Table 13.1.   Examples of possible inquiry situations.

Opening Meeting Agenda

The last duty of the team leader is to prepare the opening meeting, if one is held. (Chapter 14 explains how to conduct an opening meeting.) The team leader lists the items to be covered, with a few keywords or notes for each item. Since this document is generally not subject to distribution, a handwritten, point form document is adequate.

‖ Chapter 14 ‖

Inquiry and Conclusions

Duration

The inquiry and conclusions phase, the second phase of a typical internal audit (see Figure 14.1), starts with the opening meeting or its equivalent in the absence of such a meeting. It ends with the closing meeting. It generally is the most intense phase and is usually very stressful for inexperienced auditors. It can last from a half-day to a couple of days.

Purpose of the Inquiry

The inquiry is at the heart of the audit: good preparation is essential for an effective inquiry, whose conclusions are contained in the audit report. Within a short span of time, the auditors must:

1. Obtain the maximum relevant information.
2. Draw conclusions on the compliance of activities.
3. Judge the effectiveness of the audited processes, if an audit objective.
4. Propose changes that could really improve processes' effectiveness, if included in their mandate.

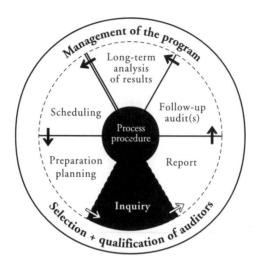

Figure 14.1. Inquiry phase in model.

Resources

Although an inquiry is not an entertainment show, a quick comparison will help understand the intensity of the inquiry. Like a show, the date, time, place, and duration have been determined; there is not much room for errors—only for minor adjustments during the performance. The actors must leave when the time is over—no curtain-call, no standing ovation.

It is perfectly normal for an auditor to be nervous. With respect to this, what is the difference between a beginner and a seasoned auditor? The latter knows that stage fright is an important part of the audit and that the absence of it is ominous.

Because of its intensity, this inquiry requires a lot of energy from each auditor, even more from the team leader. For this reason, each auditor must organize the day preceding the audit so as to be fit and alert for the inquiry. The comparison ends here.

The auditee also contributes resources to the success of this phase. Each unit must prepare for a few employees to provide information to the auditors, with an inevitable impact on the work rhythm or schedule in the department.

Inputs

Each auditor will carry into an inquiry:

+ Audit notification, with the schedule of inquiry activities
+ Audit checklist, or the applicable sections
+ Quality manual
+ Documentation describing the audited processes

and will have quick access, as needed, to:

+ Standards, codes, laws, and regulations that apply to the sector
+ The area's work instructions

Outputs

The auditors will not necessarily create new documents during this phase, with the exception of:

+ A description of the audit findings
+ The final audit report if the audit process requires that the audit report be submitted at the closing meeting

The first important output is the factual information (observations, notes, findings, references) contained in the audit checklists. This can be supplemented with copies of documents containing such information.

The second important output consists of the information, usually handwritten notes, used to present the audit conclusions at the closing meeting. This information will be used in the following phase to produce the audit report.

Opening Meeting

Purpose

Holding an opening meeting is a must in an external audit, such as a supplier or a registration audit. This first on-site activity has many objectives:

+ Introduce each other.
+ Confirm the objective and scope of the audit.
+ Confirm the logistical arrangements, as well as the availability of personnel.
+ Explain in general terms how system auditors work.
+ Clarify any relevant concerns.

In an internal audit, things can and should be done differently. For an audit of the entire quality system, an opening meeting helps ensure that the inquiry is on the right track.

On the other hand, if a small audit team has a mandate to perform a partial audit, lasting no more than one day, a formal opening meeting may not be useful, especially if the organization has been carrying out internal audits for years. In such a case, the audit would start with a short meeting of the auditors with the audited unit manager, in order to confirm the availability of personnel.

Holding of the Meeting

The meeting should last a few minutes in the simplest case, no more than 20 minutes for an audit of the entire quality system. The team leader chairs the meeting. The following three items should be on the agenda of any opening meeting:

1. Confirmation of the objective and scope of the audit
2. Confirmation of the availability of personnel
3. Clarification of any relevant concerns

Other items can be added, such as:

+ The team leader may have to introduce him- or herself, or introduce members of the team.
+ It may be necessary to explain the presence of observers on the team.
+ It is useful to explain the general audit methodology, if the auditee is going through a first audit.

Information Collection

Information collection is the one that is most dependent on auditor skills, attitudes, and behaviors. And, like an entertainment performance, it is the most difficult to teach. One can learn only by doing it and become efficient by doing it often. And the skills wear off when one stops doing it. It is difficult because:

+ The auditor is interacting with an uninterrupted series of persons, each interaction calling for all communication skills.

+ The auditor has to manage conflicting needs—for example, by listening attentively to what is being said while taking notes of audit evidence.

+ The auditor must constantly alternate between two communication levels:

  1. The contents—that is, the facts, evidence, results, and trails to follow
  2. The environment—that is, the nature of the interaction, the data collection process, and the progression status to ensure adequate coverage in the allocated timeframe

Logistical Aspects

"When in Rome, do as the Romans do" says the proverb. For an internal auditor, this implies complying with the rules and customs of the audited sector.

Physical Looks

The internal auditor should select clothing that is appropriate to the audited sector, without going overboard. A pin-striped suit is not appropriate in a transformed products environment, and neither are worn-out jeans. Adequate clothes will not detract the auditor and the auditee from the task of collecting relevant information.

If an internal auditor looks different when auditing, so much the better: that tells the other employees that the auditor is not available to address usual job concerns while auditing. If the external look cannot be different—for example, when uniforms must be worn—it may be beneficial to use another method that will communicate that the employee-auditor is assigned to a task requiring full attention. Some organizations propose a sticker that the auditor can affix to the clothing or safety hat. An example is shown in Figure 14.2.

Figure 14.2. Sticker.

Working Hours

In some organizations, different groups have different working hours. For example, office hours are from 9 to 5, and shop floor hours are from 7 to 4 or on shifts. An auditor adapts to the working hours of the audited sector.

Health and Safety

Knowing that an inquiry can be negatively perceived, an auditor does not open his or her flanks to criticism and should have a faultless approach to health and safety requirements. The auditor should wear or carry any accessory that is required in the audited sector and should abide by the same rules as the other employees, unless this prevents the achievement of audit objectives.

General Technique for Data Collection

Most auditors collect process information in two steps. First they ask that the overall process be explained and how it is related to other upstream and downstream processes. The explanation confirms the understanding of the process, and it can reveal deviations from the documentation. In this first step, the auditor generally does not need to take notes, using all his or her attention to forge a clear image of the process as described.

Second, auditors explore activities within the process for which they ask to see evidence, such as witnessing activities or verifying documents. At this point, it is generally accepted that the auditor takes notes. If the note-taking creates uneasiness, explain the purpose of the notes. Note *all* your observations, not only the problems. For each activity, close the loop with a summary describing what you understand.

For activities or documents the auditor wants to see, he or she can select examples randomly but can also follow an "audit trail" from one end to the other:

Example 1: In the purchasing process, for a selected purchased product, the auditor would ask to see the specifications, a requisition, the purchase order, the waybill or delivery notice, and the receiving inspection report for a specific purchase order.

Example 2: For a given measuring instrument, randomly selected from the list, the auditor would ask to see the calibration procedure, the last calibration results, and the identification of the reference standard used. The auditor would then continue with the calibration procedure and results for the reference standard, and so on until the auditor reached purchased calibration services traceable to national or international standards, for which the auditor would want to see some confidence in the quality of the service.

Following an audit trail enables the auditor to verify the consistency of the data in a system.

Reverse Technique

The previous technique is often referred to as "top-down," as the auditor starts with an overview of a process and then works through the details. In some cases, the "bottom-up" technique is preferable, particularly for the control of information (documents and data) and for the equipment calibration processes.

Information Control

With the top-down technique, the auditor starts with the list of applicable documents and the distribution lists and then verifies that all or some identified holders have an up-to-date copy. With the bottom-up technique, the auditor verifies that the information is available where needed and asks some employees which documents are really used. Using this information, the auditor then verifies that the employees are effectively identified on the distribution lists and that their version is up-to-date.

Calibration Control

With the top-down technique, the auditor selects examples from the instruments list and verifies that the requirements are met (procedure, frequency, status, records, and so on). With the bottom-up technique, the auditor asks employees which instruments are used or are available for use in various areas (laboratory, production, inspection) and follows the trail to purchased calibration services.

Questioning Techniques

The information obtained from an interviewee depends both on the contents of the question and on the way it is asked. Five types of questions are most often used (see Table 14.1):

1. A **personal** question invites feelings and emotions:
   - "Are you satisfied with the new instrument?"
   - "How do you react to this new quality system?"

2. A **probing** question asks for interviewee opinions:
   - "What would you recommend to solve the issue?"
   - "How should this instrument be calibrated?"

Type of Question	Expected Results
Personal	Emotions
Probing	Ideas/opinions
Open	Facts
Leading	Agreement
Closed	Confirmation

Table 14.1. Types of audit questions.

3. An **open** question tells that the auditor is looking for verifiable facts on a process or subprocess:
   - "How do you qualify your suppliers?"
   - "Which instrument is used for temperature measurements?"
   - "What do you mean by 'unacceptable document'?"

4. A **leading** question proposes a direction for the response or suggests that a previous response should be reconsidered:
   - "Should you not sign the way bill before sending it to the sales department?"

✦ "The procedure specifies that a nonconformance report be issued when results are outside specifications; do you do that?"

5. A **closed** question requires a yes/no answer:
   ✦ "Did I understand correctly that this batch was sent without the cold impact test?"
   ✦ "You actually started this press using set-up parameters that are different from those in the work package?"

In an external audit, an auditor most often uses open questions to obtain facts about the audited process. Closed questions are used occasionally to confirm that the auditor understands the situation. An auditor should confirm with a closed question any important response that is not supported by objective evidence. While external audits are formal, independent assessments, internal audits need not be as formal. In the latter case, probing and leading questions can be useful, for example in the following circumstances:

✦ Leading question. If an interviewee is very nervous and cannot respond appropriately, the auditor can use a leading question to provide some direction for a response. Very useful when used sparingly, the regular use of leading questions creates an atmosphere where the auditee learns to answer what the auditor wants to hear.

✦ Probing question. If successive audits show a persistent problem in a sector, the auditor can ask interviewees for solution ideas. The applicable ideas should appear in the audit report, with due credit to the source.

There are very few circumstances in which a personal question would be useful. Considering the risks associated with feelings and emotions in an audit context, auditors generally avoid personal questions.

Skillful use of the various types of questions does not guarantee that all responses will always be what is asked for—employees always have lots of things to express—but it increases the probability of getting the facts needed for valid audit conclusions. Although an open question asks for facts, the interviewee could still express a mix of facts, opinions, and emotions. When an auditor receives all that, he or she must react adequately and deal with the information.

Reacting to Responses

When receiving information from an interviewee, an auditor can react in many different ways, some of which can be perceived as threatening. Five categories of reaction are described here (see Table 14.2):

1. The auditor can **share** the interviewee's feelings and be carried away with anger, sadness, or any other emotion that has been expressed; this type reaction is not threatening for an interviewee but nonetheless should be avoided at all cost in an audit situation.

Type	Effect	Threat
Share	Adopt feelings	Low
Reflect	Accept feelings	Low
Restate	Understand facts	Low
Interpret	Conclude	Medium
Evaluate	Judge	High

Table 14.2. Types of auditor reactions.

2. The auditor can **reflect** the feelings, showing empathy to the interviewee's emotion, allowing the interviewee to feel understood and accepted. Because it is not threatening, this is an appropriate reaction to deal with the emotions and then go on with the audit—for example, "I understand that you can be overloaded after such a reorganization–this interview will take only a few minutes with your cooperation."

3. The auditor can **restate** perceived ideas and observed facts—a neutral demonstration that the information is understood and accepted without judgment. This is the most frequent reaction in a continuous exchange of factual information. This restating can take two forms, the *echo* and the *synthesis*.

   ✦ *Echoing* is restating factual information from the interviewee; this reaction confirms that the auditor understands the information, and it enables the conversation to move on—for example, "After verifying the customer's signature and the liquidity assets, you enter this figure on the computer input template and you wait for the calculation results" or "You believe that using red tags instead of physical segregation would free a lot of space in the receiving area without increasing risks?"

+ *Synthesizing* a series of exchanges or a long explanation is useful to conclude the collection of information on a given subprocess, but it can also be useful to control the flow of information from a voluble interviewee—for example, "In a nutshell, a helper collects samples every hour, at locations specified in this procedure, and brings them here, the laboratory, where you assign them to available technicians; are all technicians qualified for all tests?"

4. The auditor can **interpret** gathered information and draw a conclusion; although an interpretation presents a threat (in particular, if the conclusion has some negative elements), it is a type of reaction that will be used to conclude an interview or the complete audit—for example, "The laboratory calibration system seems to be compliant and effective" or "Out of 10 persons selected at random on the site, 4 personnel files do not contain evidence of proper qualification for work done today—I conclude that training control is not fully compliant and may not be effective."

5. The auditor can **evaluate** an employee, that is make a personal judgment of an employee that depends on the answer provided, and it is a very threatening reaction. Employees and systems are neither bad nor good. An auditor must avoid this reaction at all cost—for example, "The documentation system is very good—you are a top-notch employee" or "This is not a very good document—who wrote that!?" or "You cannot deny that the procedure requires that any change in the parameters must be approved—your conduct is sending a wrong message to your employees."

Communication and Behaviors

The questioning techniques and types of reactions previously described are only the two most obvious aspects of the communication between the auditor and auditee personnel. Communication is a complex subject, and there is a large selection of books, videos, and training courses in communication techniques. This book will address two more subjects and leave all other aspects to other books.

The Communication Cycle

Each interview should follow a basic, four-step cycle:

1. Opening the communication. Introduction and openers will relax the parties involved.

2. Overview of the process. Using open questions, the auditor gains a good knowledge of the audited process and of the upstream and downstream interfaces.

3. Objective evidence. Through focused questions and an examination of examples, the auditor obtains objective, verifiable evidence on the audited process.

4. Closing the communication. After a synthesis of the process, which ensures a common understanding, the auditor should leave with thanks for the interviewee's time and information.

Nonverbal Communication

During an audit, the internal auditor is temporarily in a position of relative power and is subjected to auditee scrutiny. Verbal messages tell what the auditor looks for and what the conclusions are, and body language expresses what the auditor is and how he or she feels.

Body language is a combination of posture, movement of the arms and hands, and especially eye contact that expresses interest in the verbal content. Body language is not easily controlled—it is a quasi-automatic expression of attitudes. If one cannot control body language, one can control attitudes; for example, one can decide to listen attentively to the description of the audited process, and body language will express that attentive listening.

The important thing is that body language should be consistent with the verbal message. Think of someone saying:

1. "This is very interesting," while looking at the ceiling

2. "I am very calm," while the person's hands are trembling

3. "What do you suggest?" while crossing arms

I am not saying that being nervous is unacceptable or that the auditor must show a sincere interest in all interviewee information. If the auditor is nervous, he or she should not pretend to be calm. If the auditor has no interest in the interviewee's private life, he or she should say it simply and politely.

The consistency between words and body language enables interviewees to grasp where the auditor stands, and they are likely to feel comfortable. Lack of consistency will breed nervousness and suspicion: if body language is usually different from the words, what will people "hear" when the auditor says that he or she is auditing the system, not the people?

A Few Auditing Traps

Now that we have discussed communication techniques, we will identifying a few behaviors that have trapped many internal auditors-in-training. These are the classics of the function. There are others less known and others still to be invented.

Consulting

With his experience, and being an outsider of the process, an auditor often has good and interesting ideas on what could or should be done to improve the audited process; there is a strong temptation to put forward those ideas.

Example 1. "If I were in your shoes, I would proceed like this."

Example 2. "In another organization that I know, this machine is calibrated differently and less frequently— would you like to know?"

If auditors indulge in consulting, they will reduce the overall effectiveness of the internal audits program. Maybe a good idea is not applicable in a particular case; it may be misunderstood or poorly implemented. The next time an internal auditor raises a corrective action request on the same process, he or she will be told politely that the previous internal auditor's advice was followed to the letter . . . .

If an internal audit mandate includes improvements and recommendations, these should be presented at the closing meeting, while clarifying that the auditee is free to use them.

The Useless Discussion
The amount of time spent on the inquiry and data collection is very limited; an auditor has no time to waste on discussions that do not contribute to the audit results, such as:

* Technical discussions. The auditee personnel may try to raise matters related to the auditor's regular job.
* Discussions on the quality system. A person in the audited sector may disagree with some aspects of the quality system and may prompt the auditor to justify them—especially if the auditor is from the organization's quality department.

These requests and prompts for a discussion should be turned down politely and postponed to another, more appropriate time or level.

The Go-Between
In most organizations, many employees have a longing feeling that their needs are not sufficiently cared about or that their ideas do not receive the attention they deserve. Then comes an internal audit, and those employees meet a person that has access to upper management at the closing meeting. It is only natural for them to try to use the auditor as a messenger for their needs or ideas.

Wrap-Up and Conclusion
Once the information has been collected, it is imperative to take sufficient time to analyze this information and to come to valid

conclusions that will be presented to auditee management. This activity can be expedited into one-half hour for an audit of limited scope. It can require a full half-day for a complex audit with a team comprising many auditors. Under the direction of the team leader, the auditors must come to two separate conclusions for each audited process:

1. Compliance. Are the activities actually performed in the organization compliant with the planning?
2. Effectiveness. Does the process produce the expected results?

These conclusions are necessarily qualitative, because assigning a credible numerical value is just about impossible. Each organization or auditor develops a list of expressions that will be used to describe various levels of compliance and effectiveness. In order to describe a series of decreasing levels of compliance, one could use:

+ "All verified activities conform to the XYZ procedure."
+ "Verified activities comply with the procedure, with a few minor exceptions."
+ "Most of the verified activities comply with the procedure, with some major deviations."
+ "Some activities are compliant, but many others are not done per the procedure."
+ "Most activities are performed differently than what the procedure requires."

Similarly, to describe a series of decreasing levels of effectiveness, one could use "Within the audit limitations, we can conclude that the XYZ process . . . :

+ Delivers the expected results"
+ Regularly achieves its objectives with the exception of [the isolated or minor case]"
+ Generally achieves its objectives, expect in the case in which [describe the circumstances] systematically generate an operation problem"

+ Achieves objectives with many frequent exceptions, which in the past have all lead to operation problems"

Once the auditors have formulated the general conclusions, the audit team must decide how audit findings will be reported—that is, where the organization is going to invest improvement resources. Each organization should define two levels of importance for audit findings:

1. Those that have a direct impact on the organization's quality objectives, hence related to processes effectiveness; each "major" audit finding should lead to a formal corrective action request (CAR)

2. Those that have a potential to impact processes' effectiveness but are at audit time limited to compliance to procedures; these "minor" findings should be dealt with a lighter method, although ensuring that they will be corrected before the following internal audit

In preparation for the imminent closing meeting, the team leader prepares or has other auditors prepare the following documents:

1. The closing meeting agenda, which is personally prepared by the team leader and includes all handwritten notes to ensure that all points will be covered

2. One CAR sheet for each major audit finding, which clearly describes the situation, with all useful references; an example of a typical form is shown in Figure 14.3; if the causes of the situation are known or suspected, include the description of the causes as valuable information, so as to leave ample room for the auditee to explore other causes

3. A list of minor audit findings, with enough information for the auditee and future auditors to understand the findings, even after many months

4. If the internal auditors have that mandate, recommendations to improve processes

ABC Food Store	Corrective action request # _____

Auditee/department _____

C.C. _____

Description of problem _____

_____

_____

_____

_____

_____

Procedure _____ Parag. _____

By: _____ Date: _____

Target-date for correction or decision:_____

Corrective action _____

_____

_____

_____

_____

_____

_____

_____

_____

Implementation target-date:_____

By: _____ Date: _____

Verification of implementation_____

_____

_____

By: _____ Date: _____

Figure 14.3. CAR form.

5. If specified in the internal audit process, the audit report to be submitted at the closing meeting; this could be a simple, handwritten report, such as the example shown in Figure 14.4

While preparing for the closing meeting, each auditor will have his or her own views on audit conclusions and/or on the importance of audit findings. Sometimes, these differing views cannot be reconciled through discussions. It is the team leader's responsibility to make the final call, after having listened to all the arguments. It is expected that all the auditors will rally behind the team leader, even if they do not agree with the decisions.

Closing Meeting

The audit conclusions and the corrective action requests are presented to the auditee at the closing meeting. As the team leader, who chairs the meeting, presents factual information with the audit team judgments, the meeting should last no more than one-half hour. In a smaller audit, 5 to 10 minutes could be enough.

For internal audits, the closing meeting is generally informal, especially in smaller organizations. Informal does not mean sloppy, however; it is important to present all audit results. Following is a list of items that should be addressed, as appropriate:

1. Introduction. The meeting agenda should be presented and, if the auditee is going through a first audit, an explanation of how the meeting is conducted.

2. Overall conclusions. The overall conclusions on compliance and effectiveness should be presented for each audited process, and for the entire quality system if the scope is that large.

3. Commendable features. Any area, sector, or process whose performance is well above average or beyond set objectives should be mentioned as well as the areas where major improvements were achieved since the previous audit. If

ABC
Food Store

Simple audit report

Auditee: _Reception of goods and merchandises_

C.C.: _Store manager_

Quality manager

Audited process: ___QSP-05: Receiving and storage, Aug. '97___

References: quality manual: _chapter 5, edition 2.1_

other documents: ___HACCP, 1994___

Auditor(s): _Jane_

Date(s): _March 10, 20XX_

Summary: _____

Compliance: overall, the activities are performed in accordance with procedures,

work instruction, and HACCP rules, including training manuals,

with the exception of the cold room thermometer, which has not been

verified in the last year.

Effectiveness: processes are effective, with the exceptions of :

a) the ratio of scrapped/sold iceberg lettuce is higher

   than last year, in the same period of the year;

b) the quantity of damaged canned food has increased lately, and the

   quarantine area is overflowing to other areas, where full cases are found.

Each of the two above audit findings is described on a Corrective Action Request.

By: ___Jane___   Date: ___March 10___

Figure 14.4.   Handwritten audit report.

nothing stands out to be commended, reality should not be forged to please the auditee.

4. Previous CARs. If the internal audit also has the mandate to follow-up on previous CARs, minor or major, the results of the follow-up should be presented (see chapter 16 on follow-up audits).

5. CARs. Each audit CAR should be explained and why it is considered a major finding. It is strongly suggested that at this time the auditee make a commitment with a target-date for either:

  ✦ Implementation of the corrective action, if the corrective action can be implemented with limited resources (time, personnel, material, and so on), or

  ✦ A firm decision and an action plan for corrective action, including an implementation target-date, if the corrective action requires large resources or if the decision requires further inquiry.

  If the auditee asks for a target-date that seems unreasonable, the team leader must explain why it seems unreasonable. If the team leader and the auditee cannot agree on a mutually acceptable target-date, it will be left open and the matter brought up to the internal audits program manager for resolution at a higher level. The auditee should receive a copy of the CARs (or the originals, keeping a copy for the file), either after each explanation or after the meeting. This enables the auditee to start working on the CARs right away.

6. Minor findings. A summary of the minor audit findings should be presented, specifying that they are listed in the audit report. It should be clarified that they will be verified at the next internal audit.

7. Audit report. After a simple, short audit, it is more effective to hand in the audit report at this time, even if hand-written (an example was shown in Figure 14.4). If the audit report is not submitted at the closing meeting, a date should be specified as to when it will be sent.

8. Conclusion. Before thanking all involved and closing the meeting, the team leader should open to any questions

that the auditee personnel may have, and should make a last attempt at ensuring that CARs and minor findings are well understood.

In rare circumstances, a person may question or even challenge the validity of a major audit finding/CAR, arguing that the auditor did not obtain all pertinent information. If that ever happens, an attempt to resolve it should not be made at the closing meeting. The team leader should offer to look at the missing information after the meeting, promising to cancel the CAR if the supplementary evidence warrants it.

Forgotten Findings?

It may happen, particularly in first audits, in leaving a closing meeting, stress and anxiety being dissipated, that the auditor realizes with a shock that he or she forgot to present major or minor findings. What should be done? Just adding it to the audit report is not an option (see chapter 15). There are a few alternatives, from calling a second closing meeting to forgetting them until the next internal audit. The reasonable solution lies between these two extremes.

If a major finding has been forgotten, it would be detrimental for the organization to let it go for the 6 to 12 months until the next internal audit. It would be worth calling another closing meeting and presenting all forgotten audit findings. On the other hand, if only one minor finding was forgotten, it may be more effective to just leave a note in the file for next internal audit.

Chapter 15

Audit Report

Duration

Compared with other phases, the audit report requires a very small amount of time: from a few minutes to a few hours, depending on the audit scope and its complexity. It is the third and last phase of the internal audit (see Figure 15.1). The audit report should be prepared and issued within a reasonable time-frame, but no later than one week after the audit. When the audit is of limited scope, it may be desirable to prepare the audit report at the end of the inquiry and to issue it at the closing meeting. A legible handwritten report is acceptable–even better, is a network-based electronic report.

Purpose of the Audit Report

The report's purpose is to document the audit conclusions, as well as the CARs. This information will eventually be used by management, by other internal auditors, and by registrar auditors.

Resources

The audit report could theoretically be prepared piecewise by any combination of the audit team members. For consistency and unity of style, it is desirable that a single person prepares the report; that person is usually the team leader. The task can

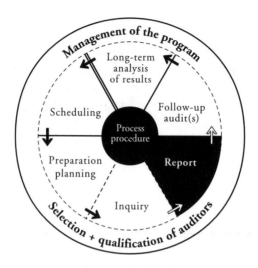

Figure 15.1. Report phase in model.

be delegated to another team member, but the team leader retains final responsibility for the report's accuracy and timely issue.

After having gone through an exciting and exhausting inquiry, there is a strong temptation to bungle this final task. This could result in an incomplete or inaccurate report, thereby reducing its impact and usefulness.

Inputs

The audit report writer uses mainly:

1. Notes that were used to conduct the closing meeting

2. Notes taken during the meeting

3. CARs and minor findings presented at the meeting

The report writer may also have to go back to the completed audit checklists, as well as to the documentation of the audited process.

Output

The output is a document that must be legible, complete, and concise, and it must accurately describe the audit results. This document must be properly approved and/or authorized, in accordance with internal rules. Each organization must have one or more documents describing the internal audit process, the audit procedure, which includes required approval levels for various documents.

Content

The content of the report is influenced by its intended uses. It formalizes what has been said and presented at the closing meeting—no more, no less. The audit results are used by:

1. Management to judge the overall effectiveness of the quality management system

2. Other internal auditors assigned to the same area, in order to understand the specifics of the area and to include the verification of previous minor findings in their audit planning

3. Registrar auditors to verify that the internal quality audit program is operating and effective

Each of these users should be able to find the information they need without going back to the detailed audit documentation.

General Information

The audit results will carry their full weight only if the eventual reader is informed about the audit objectives and scope, the sectors/groups/departments where persons have been interviewed, the name and respective function of each audit team member, the inquiry date(s), and the reference documents used (including revision status). The report distribution list is also part of the general information. Much of that information is already documented—for example, in the audit notification and schedule of activities. If the inquiry was done as planned, then the audit report can simply refer to the planning documentation.

Audit Conclusions

The conclusions should be described using words and expressions similar to those used at the closing meeting. If the audit report contains conclusions and judgment calls that are different from what was said at the meeting, it will create confusion as to what the actual results are, and it will undermine the internal auditors' credibility. This section of the report should start with any commendable feature that was commented on at the closing meeting.

Audit Findings

If a major or minor finding is canceled after the closing meeting, the report should mention what the finding was at the time of the meeting and on what grounds it was canceled.

Major Findings
It is not useful to detail every CAR, since they are already described on separate forms, copies of which were left at the closing meeting. A short phrase summarizing each CAR is sufficient.

Minor Findings
Because they are described only in the audit report, the description must be sufficiently clear and complete to enable another auditor to understand what is at stake, even after many months. Auditors often make incomplete descriptions, trying to save a half-hour, but the next internal auditor often has to spend a lot of time going back through the file before understanding the finding because of that "saved" half-hour.

Recommendations

If one objective of the audit is to propose improvements to the system or to the processes, the recommendations should appear in the audit report. The recommendations can provide the auditee with hints on the causes of CARs or on how to address them. Recommendations on process effectiveness and efficiency can also be made, even if not related to the CARs.

Appendices

Documents that add value to the audit report should be attached as appendices. One normally attaches CARs, handwritten or typed. Where there are recommendations for improvements, other documents may be useful.

Simplicity

Internal audit reports should be kept as simple as possible. In its simplest form, it can be a one-page manuscript or an electronic equivalent. In either case, a form or document template will speed the report writing.

| Chapter 16 |

Follow-Up Audit

Duration

A follow-up audit is a full-fledged audit, with very limited objectives and scope. The three basic phases of preparation/inquiry/report are performed, although in a matter of hours. Each is addressed in this chapter in a simplified version.

Purpose of a Follow-Up Audit

The objective of a follow-up audit is to confirm that the actions taken by the auditee have effectively corrected the situation that gave birth to the audit finding.

Resources

A follow-up audit is usually performed by a single auditor, preferably a member of the audit team who had previously raised and documented the finding. It usually consumes less than one hour per finding. A follow-up audit could exceptionally require more than one day, when an audit finding resulted in a corrective action that included installing new equipment and modifying many process-related requirements.

Timing

Follow-up audits can be scheduled in direct relationship with each CAR's implementation target-date, which can be from a few weeks to many months after the CAR was issued, depending on the nature of the corrective actions. Another approach is to systematically verify the implementation of corrective actions at a subsequent regular internal audit, which is done 6 to 18 months after the previous audit.

Planning

Preparing the follow-up audit consists of understanding the nature and extent of the original audit finding. This can be accomplished by reading the CAR and the audit report. If they do not contain enough information, it is necessary to go back to the inquiry notes and to the process documentation.

Inquiry

With the auditee response in the CAR, the auditor will determine:

+ The real actions that were decided to address the audit finding
+ The actual changes made to the quality management system in order to find out if they are in line with the decisions made and if they eliminate the audit finding

The inquiry can be conducted in an office if the corrective action consists of modifying documentation. In many cases, though, collecting data and information will be required in order to determine if the corrective action is adequate and effective.

In most cases, the inquiry results confirm that the decision has been implemented and that the resulting changes effectively resolve the audit finding. Sometimes, this is not the case because either the decision did not address the real cause or the implementation has not been completed. Here the auditor has a choice of actions:

+ The CAR is closed and a new CAR is issued.
+ The auditee is given (in writing) an extension for the implementation.

In an internal follow-up audit, opening and closing meetings are not usually held, but it is a good practice to communicate the results verbally to auditee management.

Report

Forms used to document CARs usually have a space in the lower part to document the follow-up results—this is the audit report. The auditor describes what has been verified, followed with one of the three following conclusions:

1. The corrective actions have corrected the finding.

2. The corrective actions are not completely implemented, and a new target-date is written down.

3. The corrective actions have had little effect on the situation.

In the third case, another CAR will be issued, describing the observations made during the follow-up inquiry. This second CAR is presented to the auditee management. Both CARs should be referenced to each other in order to maintain an audit trail.

| Conclusion |

It is certainly desirable that internal quality audits evolve beyond the "necessary evil to maintain registration" to a status of management tool, which will provide valid and credible information necessary for sound management decisions. But this information does not come without cost: the organization has to make commitments *and* invest resources.

First, the management has to create a favorable environment by accepting the risks associated with it. Second, the management must define the objectives of the internal audits program, decide on preferred approaches, specify the necessary auditor qualifications, determine audit methods and procedures, and allocate resources. Once that is done, the auditors can fully profit the organization.

An internal audit is composed of activities, many of which are very subjective. Audit methods and procedures dampen this subjectivity, but one should always remember that the *quality* of audit results rests essentially on the *competence* of the auditors. Having pre-established methods for obtaining and maintaining auditor competence is one of the key elements of an effective internal quality audit program.

| INDEX |

135